GCSE Edexcel
Biology
The Revision Guide

This book is for anyone doing **GCSE Edexcel Biology**.
It covers everything you'll need for your year 10 and 11 exams.

GCSE Science is all about **understanding how science works**.
And not only that — understanding it well enough to be able to **question**
what you hear on TV and read in the papers.

But you can't do that without a fair chunk of **background knowledge**. Hmm, tricky.

Happily this CGP book includes all the **science facts** you need to learn,
and shows you how they work in the **real world**. And in true CGP style,
we've explained it all as **clearly and concisely** as possible.

It's also got some daft bits in to try and make the whole
experience at least vaguely entertaining for you.

What CGP is all about

Our sole aim here at CGP is to produce the highest
quality books — carefully written, immaculately presented
and dangerously close to being funny.

Then we work our socks off to get them
out to you — at the cheapest possible prices.

Contents

Published by CGP

From original material by Richard Parsons.

Editors:
Charlotte Burrows, Mary Falkner, Ben Fletcher, Rosie McCurrie.

Contributors:
James Foster, Adrian Schmit, Sophie Watkins.

ISBN: 978 1 84762 606 6

With thanks to Helen Brace, Katie Braid, Janet Cruse-Sawyer, David Hickinson,
Sue Hocking, and Hayley Thompson for the proofreading.
With thanks to Laura Jakubowski for the copyright research.

With thanks to Getty Images for permission to use the image on page 61.

Every effort has been made to locate copyright holders and obtain permission to reproduce
sources. For those sources where it has been difficult to trace the originator of the work, we would
be grateful for information. If any copyright holder would like us to make an amendment to the
acknowledgements, please notify us and we will gladly update the book at the next reprint.
Thank you.

Groovy website: www.cgpbooks.co.uk

Printed by Elanders Ltd, Newcastle upon Tyne.
Jolly bits of clipart from CorelDRAW®

The Scientific Process

You need to know a few things about how the world of science works. First up is the <u>scientific process</u> — how a scientist's <u>mad idea</u> turns into a <u>widely accepted theory</u>.

Scientists Come Up with <u>Hypotheses</u> — Then <u>Test</u> <u>Them</u>

Hundreds of years ago, we thought demons caused illness.

1) Scientists try to <u>explain</u> things. Everything.

2) They start by <u>observing</u> something they don't understand — it could be anything, e.g. planets in the sky, a person suffering from an illness, what matter is made of... anything.

3) Then, they come up with a <u>hypothesis</u> — a <u>possible explanation</u> for what they've observed.

4) The next step is to <u>test</u> whether the hypothesis might be <u>right or not</u> — this involves <u>gathering evidence</u> (i.e. <u>data</u> from <u>investigations</u>).

5) To gather evidence the scientist uses the hypothesis to make a <u>prediction</u> — a statement based on the hypothesis that can be <u>tested</u>.

6) If data from experiments or studies <u>backs up the prediction</u>, you're one step closer to figuring out if the hypothesis is true.

Other Scientists Will <u>Test</u> the Hypotheses Too

1) <u>Other</u> scientists will use the hypothesis to make their <u>own predictions</u>, and carry out their <u>own experiments</u> or studies.

2) They'll also try to <u>reproduce</u> the original investigations to check the results.

3) And if <u>all the experiments</u> in the world back up the hypothesis, then scientists start to think it's <u>true</u>.

4) However, if a scientist somewhere in the world does an experiment that <u>doesn't</u> fit with the hypothesis (and other scientists can <u>reproduce</u> these results), then the hypothesis is in trouble.

5) When this happens, scientists have to come up with a new hypothesis (maybe a <u>modification</u> of the old hypothesis, or maybe a completely <u>new</u> one).

Then we thought it was caused by 'bad blood' (and treated it with leeches).

If <u>Evidence</u> Supports a Hypothesis, It's <u>Accepted</u> — for Now

1) If pretty much every scientist in the world believes a hypothesis to be true because experiments back it up, then it usually goes in the <u>textbooks</u> for students to learn.

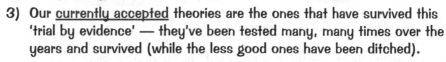

Now we know most illnesses are due to microorganisms.

2) Accepted hypotheses are often referred to as <u>theories</u>.

3) Our <u>currently accepted</u> theories are the ones that have survived this 'trial by evidence' — they've been tested many, many times over the years and survived (while the less good ones have been ditched).

4) However... they never, <u>never</u> become hard and fast, totally indisputable <u>fact</u>. You can never know... it'd only take <u>one</u> odd, totally inexplicable result, and the hypothesising and testing would start all over again.

<u>You expect me to believe that — then show me the evidence...</u>

Scientific <u>ideas</u> are <u>changing</u> all the time as a result of <u>new evidence</u> being uncovered. It's the role of the <u>scientific community</u> (all the world's scientists) to <u>test</u> and <u>evaluate</u> these ideas and decide whether or not they should be <u>accepted</u> as theories — so you don't have to waste your time learning stuff that's absolute rubbish.

Data and the Limits of Science

Evidence is the key to science, but it's not all equally good. How it's gathered affects how trustworthy it is.

Your Data's Got to Be Good

There's more about variables and fair tests on page 3.

1) Results from controlled experiments in laboratories are great. A lab is the easiest place to control variables so that they're all kept constant (except for the one you're investigating). This makes it easier to carry out a fair test.

2) For things that you can't investigate in the lab (e.g. the link between smoking and cancer) you conduct scientific studies. As many of the variables as possible are controlled, to make it a fair test.

3) Data from large samples is better than data from small samples. A sample should be representative of the whole population (i.e. it should share as many of the various characteristics in the population as possible) — a small sample can't do that as well as a big 'un.

4) Old wives' tales, rumours, hearsay, "what someone said", and so on, should be taken with a pinch of salt. Without any evidence they're NOT scientific — they're just opinions.

Evidence Needs to be Reliable (Reproducible) and Valid

RELIABLE means that the data can be reproduced by others.

EXAMPLE: In 1998, a scientist claimed that he'd found a link between the MMR (measles, mumps and rubella) vaccine and autism. However, no other scientist has been able to repeat the results since — they just weren't reliable. Because they couldn't be repeated, no-one has any reason to believe them.

VALID means that the data is reliable AND answers the original question.

EXAMPLE: DO OVERHEAD POWER LINES CAUSE CANCER?
Some studies have found that children who live near power lines are more likely to develop cancer.
What they've actually found is a correlation (relationship) between "presence of power lines" and "incidence of cancer" — they've found that as one changes, so does the other. But this evidence isn't enough to say that the power lines cause cancer, as other explanations might be possible (e.g. power lines are often near busy roads, so pollution might be to blame). These studies don't show a definite link and so don't answer the original question.

Some Questions Are Unanswered by Science, Some Are Unanswerable

1) At the moment scientists don't all agree on some things (e.g. the likely impacts of global warming, or what the Universe is made of) because there isn't enough reliable and valid evidence.

2) But eventually, we'll probably answer these questions once and for all. We just need more evidence.

3) However, the question of whether something is morally or ethically right or wrong can't be answered by more experiments — there is no "right" or "wrong" answer.

4) The best we can do is get a consensus from society — a judgement that most people are more or less happy to live by. Science can provide more information to help people make this judgement, and the judgement might change over time. But in the end it's up to people and their conscience.

5) Decisions about how science is used can also be influenced by lots of other factors (e.g. economic, social, environmental and ethical issues).

It's hard to be definite about anything...

... but getting lots of evidence from different studies, that all points the same way, can convince people.

Planning Experiments

That's all the dull stuff about the world of science over — now to the hands-on part. The next few pages show how <u>experiments</u> should be carried out — by both <u>professional scientists</u> and <u>you</u>.

An Experiment Must be a Fair Test

1) One of the most important parts of planning an experiment is making sure that the <u>evidence</u> you collect is <u>valid</u> and <u>reliable</u> (see page 2). This means that your experiment must be a <u>fair test</u>.

2) The only way to make it a fair test is to <u>change</u> only <u>one variable</u> (factor) in the experiment. All the <u>other variables</u> should <u>be controlled</u> — they should <u>stay exactly the same</u> throughout the experiment and each time the experiment is repeated.

3) For example, if you're looking at the effect of <u>temperature</u> on the rate of an enzyme-controlled reaction you need to keep the <u>pH</u> the same each time (otherwise you won't know if any change in the rate of reaction is caused by the change in temperature, or the change in pH).

The Equipment Used Has to be Right for the Job

When you're planning an experiment, you need to make sure you choose the <u>right equipment</u>. For example, the measuring equipment you use has to be <u>sensitive enough</u> to accurately measure the chemicals you're using, e.g. if you need to measure out 11 ml of a liquid, you'll need to use a measuring cylinder that can measure to 1 ml, not 5 or 10 ml.

An Experiment Must be Safe

1) Part of planning an experiment is making sure that it's <u>safe</u>.

2) There are lots of <u>hazards</u> you could be faced with during an experiment, e.g. <u>microorganisms</u>, <u>chemicals</u>, <u>electricity</u>, <u>gas</u> and <u>fire</u>.

3) You should always make sure that you <u>identify</u> all the hazards that you might encounter.

4) You should also come up with ways of <u>reducing the risks</u> from the hazards you've identified.

5) One way of doing this is to carry out a <u>risk assessment</u>:

For an experiment involving a <u>Bunsen burner</u>, the risk assessment might be something like this:

<u>Hazard</u>: Bunsen burner is a fire risk.
<u>Precautions</u>:
- Keep flammable chemicals away from the Bunsen.
- Never leave the Bunsen unattended when lit.
- Always turn on the yellow safety flame when not in use.

Repeats affect Reliability, and Range of Measurements affects Validity

1) One way to make data <u>more reliable</u> is to <u>repeat</u> the measurements and take an <u>average</u> (see next page).

2) Also, the <u>range of data</u> collected has to be <u>suitable</u>, and you need to take <u>enough measurements</u> throughout the <u>whole</u> of the range — otherwise you won't be able to identify the <u>pattern</u> you're looking for. For example, if your hypothesis is that temperature affects the rate of an enzyme-controlled reaction, you'd need to measure the rate of reaction at a wide range of temperatures, e.g. 0 °C to 50 °C, and in 5 °C steps throughout the range.

3) If the range isn't big enough, or you don't take enough measurements throughout the range, your data <u>won't</u> be <u>valid</u> for the <u>hypothesis</u> you're supposed to be testing.

Take a look back at page 2 if you can't remember what reliability and validity are.

Reliable data — it won't ever forget your birthday...

All this stuff is really important — without <u>good quality</u> data an investigation will be totally <u>meaningless</u>. So give this page a read through a couple of times and your data will be the envy of the whole scientific community.

Collecting, Processing and Presenting Data

After you've collected your data you'll have <u>oodles of info</u> that you have to <u>make some kind of sense of</u>. You need to <u>process</u> and <u>present</u> it so you can look for <u>patterns</u> and <u>relationships</u> in it.

Data Needs to be Organised

1) <u>Tables</u> are dead useful for <u>recording results</u> and <u>organising data</u>.

2) When you draw a table, make sure that <u>each column</u> has a <u>heading</u> and that you've included the <u>units</u>.

3) Annoyingly, tables are about as useful as a chocolate teapot for showing <u>patterns</u> or <u>relationships</u> in data. You need to use some kind of graph for that (see below).

Check For Mistakes Made When Collecting Data

1) When you've collected all the results for an experiment, you should have a look to see if there are any results that <u>don't seem to fit</u> in with the rest.

2) Most results vary a bit, but any that are totally different are called <u>anomalous results</u>.

3) If you ever get any anomalous results, you should investigate them to try to <u>work out what happened</u>. If you can work out what happened (e.g. you measured something wrong) you can <u>ignore</u> them when processing and presenting your data.

Data Can be Processed Using a Bit of Maths

1) When you've done repeats of an experiment you should always calculate the <u>mean</u> (average). To do this <u>ADD TOGETHER</u> all the data values and <u>DIVIDE</u> by the total number of values in the sample.

2) You might also need to calculate the <u>range</u> (how spread out the data is). To do this find the <u>LARGEST</u> number and <u>SUBTRACT</u> the <u>SMALLEST</u> number from it. *Ignore anomalous results when calculating these.*

EXAMPLE:

Test tube	Repeat 1 (g)	Repeat 2 (g)	Repeat 3 (g)	Mean (g)	Range (g)
A	28	37	32	(28 + 37 + 32) ÷ 3 = 32.3	37 – 28 = 9
B	47	51	60	(47 + 51 + 60) ÷ 3 = 52.7	60 – 47 = 13
C	68	72	70	(68 + 72 + 70) ÷ 3 = 70.0	72 – 68 = 4

If Your Data Comes in Categories, Present It in a Bar Chart

1) If one of the variables is <u>categoric</u> (comes in distinct categories, e.g. blood types, eye colour) you should use a <u>bar chart</u> to display the data.

2) You can also use a bar chart if one of the variables is <u>discrete</u> (the data can only take whole values and there are no in-between ones, e.g. number of people is discrete because you can't have half a person).

3) There are some <u>golden rules</u> you need to follow for <u>drawing</u> bar charts:

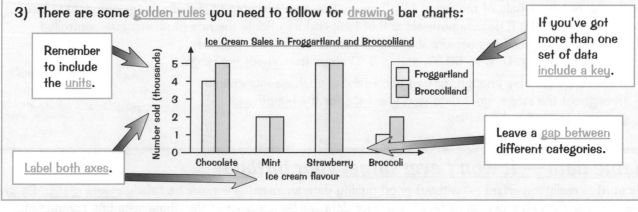

Remember to include the <u>units</u>.

If you've got more than one set of data <u>include a key</u>.

Label both axes.

Leave a <u>gap between</u> different categories.

Ice Cream Sales in Froggartland and Broccoliland

Number sold (thousands)

Chocolate   Mint   Strawberry   Broccoli
Ice cream flavour

Froggartland
Broccoliland

Collecting, Processing and Presenting Data

If Your Data is Continuous, Plot a Line Graph

1) If <u>both</u> the variables are <u>continuous</u> (numerical data that can have any value within a range, e.g. length, volume, temperature) you should use a <u>line graph</u> to display the data.

2) Here are the <u>rules</u> for <u>drawing</u> line graphs:

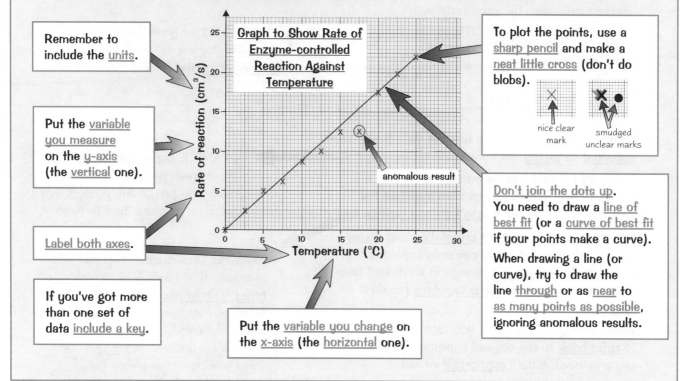

Remember to include the <u>units</u>.

Put the <u>variable</u> <u>you measure</u> on the <u>y-axis</u> (the <u>vertical</u> one).

Label both axes.

If you've got more than one set of data <u>include a key</u>.

Graph to Show Rate of Enzyme-controlled Reaction Against Temperature

anomalous result

Put the <u>variable you change</u> on the <u>x-axis</u> (the <u>horizontal</u> one).

To plot the points, use a <u>sharp pencil</u> and make a <u>neat little cross</u> (don't do blobs).

nice clear mark

smudged unclear marks

<u>Don't join the dots up.</u> You need to draw a <u>line of best fit</u> (or a <u>curve of best fit</u> if your points make a curve).

When drawing a line (or curve), try to draw the line <u>through</u> or as <u>near</u> to <u>as many points as possible</u>, ignoring anomalous results.

Line Graphs Can Show Relationships in Data

1) Line graphs are used to <u>show the relationship</u> between two variables (just like other graphs).

2) Data can show <u>three</u> different types of correlation (relationship):

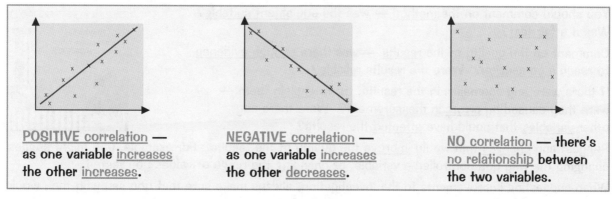

<u>POSITIVE</u> correlation — as one variable <u>increases</u> the other <u>increases</u>.

<u>NEGATIVE</u> correlation — as one variable <u>increases</u> the other <u>decreases</u>.

<u>NO</u> correlation — there's <u>no relationship</u> between the two variables.

3) You've got to be careful not to <u>confuse correlation</u> with <u>cause</u> though. A <u>correlation</u> just means that there's a <u>relationship</u> between two variables. It <u>doesn't mean</u> that the change in one variable is <u>causing</u> the change in the other (there might be <u>other factors</u> involved).

There's a positive correlation between age of man and length of nose hair...

<u>Collect</u>, <u>process</u>, <u>present</u>... data's like a difficult child — it needs a lot of attention. Go on, make it happy.

Drawing Conclusions and Evaluating

At the end of an experiment, the conclusion and evaluation are waiting. Don't worry, they won't bite.

You Can Only Conclude _What the Data Shows and NO MORE_

1) Drawing a conclusion can be quite straightforward — just look at your data and say what pattern you see between the variables.

> **EXAMPLE:** The table below shows the heights of pea plant seedlings grown for three weeks with different fertilisers.
>
> | Fertiliser | Mean growth / mm |
> |------------|------------------|
> | A | 13.5 |
> | B | 19.5 |
> | No fertiliser | 5.5 |
>
> **CONCLUSION:** Fertiliser underline{B} makes pea plant seedlings grow taller over a three week period than fertiliser A.

2) However, you also need to use the data that's been collected to justify the conclusion (back it up).

> **EXAMPLE** continued... Over the three week period, Fertiliser B made the pea plants grow 6 mm more on average than fertiliser A.

3) There are some things to watch out for too — it's important that the conclusion matches the data it's based on and doesn't go any further.

4) Remember not to confuse correlation and cause (see previous page). You can only conclude that one variable is causing a change in another if you have controlled all the other variables (made it a fair test).

5) When writing a conclusion you also need to refer back to the original hypothesis — say whether the data supports it or not.

6) Then explain what's been found using your own scientific knowledge (what you've learnt in class).

> **EXAMPLE** continued... You can't conclude that fertiliser B makes any other type of plant grow taller than fertiliser A — the results could be totally different. Also, you can't make any conclusions beyond the three weeks — the plants could drop dead.

Evaluation — _Describe How You Could Improve the Investigation_

1) You should comment on the method — was the equipment suitable? Was it a fair test?

2) Comment on the quality of the results — was there enough evidence to reach a conclusion? Were the results reliable?

> I'd value this E somewhere in the region of 250-300k

3) If there were any anomalies in the results, try to explain them — were they caused by errors in measurement? Were there any other variables that could have affected the results?

4) Suggest any changes that would improve the quality of the results. For example, you might suggest changing the way you controlled a variable, or changing the range of values you tested.

5) When suggesting improvements to the investigation, always make sure that you say why they would make the results better.

Evaluation — _next time, I will make sure I don't burn the lab down..._

I know it doesn't seem very nice, but writing about where you went wrong is an important skill — it shows you've got a really good understanding of what the investigation was about. It's difficult for me — I'm always right.

The Controlled Assessment

You'll probably carry out a few investigations as you go through the course, but at some point you'll have to do the one that counts... the <u>controlled assessment</u>. Here's a bit about it...

The Controlled Assessment *is Split into Three Parts*

Part A — Planning

For this part you'll be given some information about a topic. Then you'll have to develop a <u>hypothesis</u> and <u>plan an experiment</u> to <u>test it</u>. Write a <u>method</u> in a logical <u>step-by-step</u> order — you'll need to decide:

1) What <u>variables</u> you're going to <u>control</u> — and <u>how</u> you're going to control them.

2) What <u>equipment</u> to use — and say <u>why</u> you've chosen each bit of kit.

3) What <u>risks</u> are involved in the experiment — and say <u>how</u> you're going to <u>reduce</u> each of them.

4) The <u>range of measurements</u> you're going to take — and say <u>why</u> you've chosen that range.

5) How many times you'll <u>repeat</u> each measurement. You should do <u>at least two</u> repeats to make your data <u>more reliable</u>.

There's lots of help on all of these things on page 3.

You'll also need to say why your method is <u>suitable</u> for testing the hypothesis.

Part B — Observations

For Part B you'll be testing the hypothesis you developed in Part A by <u>carrying out the experiment</u> you planned. You'll need to:

1) Take an appropriate <u>number</u> and <u>range</u> of measurements (see page 3).

2) <u>Repeat</u> your measurements to get more <u>reliable data</u> (if possible) — <u>two times</u> is a good idea.

3) <u>Record</u> your data clearly in a nice, neat <u>table</u> (see page 4 for table tips).

Also, you'll need to find some <u>secondary data</u> (data collected by other people) that's relevant to the hypothesis. Make sure you say <u>where</u> you got the data from, and say <u>how good quality</u> the source was.

Part C — Conclusions

This part involves <u>processing</u> data, <u>presenting</u> data, drawing <u>conclusions</u> and <u>evaluating</u>. You'll have to do these things for your data (<u>primary data</u>), but also for the <u>secondary data</u> you collected in Part B. You'll need to:

1) <u>Process all the data</u> (both primary and secondary), e.g. calculate the mean (see page 4).

2) <u>Present all the data</u> using the right type of <u>graph</u> for each (see pages 4-5 for help with this).

3) Identify any <u>anomalous results</u> and explain why you didn't include them when you processed and presented your data (they'd reduce the validity of your results). If there <u>aren't</u> any anomalous results, then you need to <u>say so</u>.

4) Write <u>conclusions</u> that cover all the data (see previous page for what to say). Make sure you <u>back up</u> your conclusions using the data, say <u>whether the conclusions support the hypothesis</u> or not and <u>explain what's been found</u> using your own knowledge.

5) Write an <u>evaluation</u> (see previous page for what to include). Don't forget to say <u>how</u> the method affected the results, and how any improvements would make the results better.

6) Use your evaluation to say how <u>confident</u> you are in your conclusions. Think about <u>other evidence</u> that you could collect to give <u>stronger support</u> for your conclusions.

Keep your assessment under control — read this page...

Pretty straightforward, eh? As long as you've <u>learnt everything</u> on the previous few pages, you should be fine. Make sure you <u>know</u> each section like the <u>back of your hand</u> before you come to do the assessment itself.

B1 Topic 1 — Variation

Classification

It seems to be a basic human urge to want to classify things — that's the case in biology anyway...

Classification is Organising Living Organisms into Groups

1) Biologists <u>classify</u> organisms into groups based on how <u>closely related</u> they are to one another.

2) All living things are divided into <u>five kingdoms</u> — <u>plants</u>, <u>animals</u>, <u>fungi</u>, <u>protoctists</u> and <u>prokaryotes</u>.

3) Plants contain <u>chlorophyll</u> and are <u>autotrophs</u> (they're able to <u>make their own food</u> by photosynthesis). They're <u>multicellular</u> and have rigid <u>cell walls</u>, which support the cells.

4) Animals are <u>heterotrophs</u> — they <u>can't</u> make their own food, so they have to <u>move about</u> and find things to eat, e.g. plants. Animals are <u>multicellular</u>, like plants, but they <u>don't</u> have <u>cell walls</u> or <u>chlorophyll</u>.

5) Fungi are <u>saprophytes</u> — they feed off <u>dead organisms</u> and <u>decaying material</u> (nice). They're <u>multicellular</u> and have a <u>cell wall</u>, but <u>don't</u> have <u>chlorophyll</u>.

6) Protoctists are <u>unicellular</u> (single-celled) and have a <u>nucleus</u>, e.g. <u>algae</u>.

7) Prokaryotes are also <u>unicellular</u> but they <u>don't</u> have a <u>nucleus</u>, e.g. <u>bacteria</u>.

8) Sometimes it's hard to classify organisms. For example, most scientists think <u>viruses</u> are <u>non-living</u>, so they can't be placed in <u>any kingdom</u>.

9) Kingdoms are <u>subdivided</u> into smaller and smaller groups of organisms that have <u>common features</u>.

> The phylum <u>Chordata</u> is made up of animals that all have a <u>supporting rod-like structure</u> that goes up the back of the body, e.g. this forms the <u>backbone</u> in vertebrates (see below).

Kingdom
Phylum
Class
Order
Family
Genus
Species

Etc.

So a genus contains several species with similar features.

Animals are Divided into Vertebrates and Invertebrates

Vertebrates have a <u>backbone</u> and an <u>internal skeleton</u> — invertebrates don't (some have an <u>external skeleton</u>).
<u>Vertebrates</u> are divided into five groups, called <u>classes</u> — fish, amphibians, reptiles, birds and mammals.
Scientists divide vertebrates into these classes based on <u>three main things</u>:

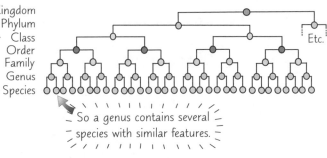

1) How they absorb OXYGEN — through <u>lungs</u> (e.g. birds), <u>gills</u> (e.g. fish) or <u>skin</u> (e.g. amphibians).

2) How they REPRODUCE — whether <u>fertilisation</u> occurs <u>internally</u> (e.g. mammals) or <u>externally</u> (e.g. fish). Also whether they are <u>oviparous</u> (lay eggs, e.g. reptiles) or <u>viviparous</u> (give birth to <u>live young</u> which are <u>fed milk</u> by the mother, e.g. mammals).

3) How they REGULATE THEIR INTERNAL BODY TEMPERATURE — whether they're <u>homeotherms</u> — this means they're '<u>warm-blooded</u>' as their body temperature is kept constant by homeostasis, e.g. mammals. Or, whether they're <u>poikilotherms</u> — this means they're '<u>cold-blooded</u>' as they're body temperature changes with external temperature, e.g. reptiles.

The <u>rules</u> of the classification system were made up using the animals and plants that were <u>known</u> <u>about</u> at the time. Sometimes <u>newly discovered species</u> don't really <u>fit</u> into any of the categories.

E.g. the <u>duck-billed platypus</u> is an odd-looking thing, with a bill like a <u>duck</u> and a tail like a <u>beaver</u>. It's classed as a <u>mammal</u> because it has similar features to other mammals (e.g. it's homeothermic and suckles its young). BUT it lays eggs, whereas mammals usually give birth to live young. Hmm.

Talent shows are about organising singing organisms into groups...

Everything is grouped according to similarities and differences. The problem is that we make our groups based on the species we've <u>already discovered</u> — but when a new one turns up, it may not fit in very conveniently.

More on Classification

Classification isn't the most exciting thing ever (unlike doughnuts), but there's a bit more you need to know...

Accurate Classification isn't Always Easy...

Organisms are the same species if they can interbreed to produce fertile offspring. But sometimes it's not easy to put organisms into nice neat boxes called species. Here are some examples why:

1) Not all organisms interbreed like the species definition says — some reproduce asexually but they're still the same species.

2) If a male from one species breeds with a female from a second species you'll get a hybrid and these can be fertile. E.g. many duck species interbreed to produce fertile hybrids (e.g. the Mallard with the Yellow-Billed Duck). This contradicts the species definition — according to it, all these ducks should be the same species. However, they're not because they're really different in many other ways, e.g. in genetics.

3) You'd expect members of the same species to look pretty similar. But there can be a lot of variation within a species. E.g. there are tons of breeds of dogs that look wildly different, but they're all the same species.

4) A ring species is a group of related populations that live in neighbouring areas. The populations that live next to each other can interbreed to produce fertile offspring, but populations that live further apart can't. An example is shown in the diagram. It's difficult to tell if all the populations are different species.

The Binomial System Gives Everything a Two-part Name

1) In the binomial system, each species is given a two-part Latin name. The first part refers to the genus that the organism belongs to and the second part refers to the species.

E.g. Humans are known as Homo sapiens. 'Homo' is the genus that they belong to and 'sapiens' is the species.

2) The binomial system has helped scientists to:

• Identify species — it avoids confusion where common names mean different things in different places.

• Study species — by identifying and naming species, scientists can share information on them.

• Conserve species (especially endangered species) — e.g. it's easy to presume that two similar-looking organisms are the same species, when they're actually different. This could mean that only one species is protected, whilst the other becomes extinct.

• Target conservation efforts — we can protect areas that have a great variety of different species, e.g. tropical rainforests, to prevent a huge number of species being destroyed.

Keys are Used to Identify Creatures

1) A key is a series of questions that you can use to figure out what an unknown organism is.

2) You start at question 1, and the answer to that question (which you know by looking at your mystery organism) is used to narrow down your options of what it could be.

3) As you answer more and more questions you narrow down your options further until eventually you're just left with one possible species your organism could be.

Example: A student saw the following living things in a pond. Using the key provided, work out what each organism is.

1) Can the organism produce its own food? ....YES, then it's a water lily ....NO — go to question 2
2) Does the organism have six legs? ....YES, then it's a dragonfly ....NO — go to question 3
3) Does the organism have gills? ....YES, then it's a fish ....NO, then it's a frog

Binomial system — uh oh, sounds like maths...

You might have to construct a key in an exam. The easiest way is to make each question identify one organism. E.g. if the list of organisms include a bird, you could ask "does the organism have feathers?" to identify it.

Variation

You'll probably have noticed that not all people are identical. There are reasons for this.

Organisms of the Same Species Have Differences

1) Different species look... well... different — my dog definitely doesn't look like a daisy.

2) But even organisms of the <u>same species</u> will usually look at least <u>slightly</u> different
   — e.g. in a room full of people you'll see different <u>colour hair</u>, individually <u>shaped</u>
   <u>noses</u>, a variety of <u>heights</u> etc.

3) These differences are called the <u>variation</u> within a species — and there are
   <u>two</u> causes of variation: <u>genes</u> and the <u>environment</u>.

Different Genes Cause Genetic Variation

1) All plants and animals have <u>characteristics</u> that are in some ways similar to their <u>parents'</u>
   (e.g. I've got my dad's nose, apparently).

2) This is because an organism's <u>characteristics</u> are determined by the <u>genes inherited</u> from their <u>parents</u>.
   (Genes are the <u>codes</u> inside your cells that <u>control</u> how you're made — more about these on page 14.)

3) Most animals (and quite a lot of plants) get <u>some</u> genes from the <u>mother</u> and <u>some</u> from the <u>father</u>.

4) This combining of genes from two parents causes <u>genetic variation</u> — no two of the species are
   <u>genetically identical</u> (other than identical twins).

5) Genetic variation also occurs due to <u>mutations</u> — <u>changes</u> in an organism's <u>genes</u>.
   These changes can cause differences in an organism's <u>characteristics</u>.

6) <u>Some</u> characteristics are determined <u>only</u> by genes (e.g. violet flower colour). In <u>animals</u> these
   include: <u>eye colour</u>, <u>blood group</u> and <u>inherited disorders</u> (e.g. haemophilia or cystic fibrosis).

Characteristics are also Influenced by the Environment

1) The <u>environment</u> that organisms <u>live and grow</u>
   in also causes <u>differences</u> between members
   of the same species — this is called
   <u>environmental variation</u>.

2) Environmental variation covers a <u>wide range</u> of
   differences — from <u>losing your toes</u> in a piranha
   attack, to getting a <u>suntan</u>, to having <u>yellow leaves</u>
   (never happened to me yet though), and so on.

3) <u>Environmental factors</u> that can cause variation
   include <u>diet</u>, <u>exercise</u>, <u>temperature</u>, <u>light level</u>,
   <u>amount of water</u> etc.

A plant grown on a nice sunny windowsill
would grow <u>luscious</u> and <u>green</u>.

The same plant grown in darkness
would grow <u>tall and spindly</u>
and its leaves would turn <u>yellow</u>
— these are <u>environmental variations</u>.

Characteristics caused by the environment
are called 'acquired characteristics'.

Most Characteristics are Due to Genes AND the Environment

1) <u>Most characteristics</u> (e.g. body weight, height, skin colour, condition of teeth, academic or
   athletic prowess, etc.) are determined by a <u>mixture</u> of <u>genetic</u> and <u>environmental</u> factors.

2) For example, the <u>maximum height</u> that an animal or plant could grow to is determined by its <u>genes</u>.
   But whether it actually grows that tall depends on its <u>environment</u> (e.g. how much food it gets).

My mum's got no trousers — cos I've got her jeans...

So, you are the way you are partly because of the genes you inherited off your folks. But you can't blame it <u>all</u>
on your parents, since your <u>environment</u> then takes over and begins to mould you in all sorts of ways.
In fact, it's often really tricky to decide which factor is <u>more influential</u>, your genes or the environment.

Continuous and Discontinuous Variation

I'm afraid you're not finished with variation yet — you need to know about the difference between <u>continuous</u> and <u>discontinuous</u> variation. It's not too complicated, honest...

Variation can be Continuous...

<u>Continuous variation</u> is when the individuals in a population <u>vary within a range</u> — there are <u>no distinct categories</u>, e.g. humans can be any height within a range (139 cm, 175 cm, 185.9 cm...), not just tall or short. Here are some more examples:

- <u>Animals</u> — e.g. <u>humans</u> can be any <u>mass</u> within a range.
- <u>Microorganisms</u> — e.g. the <u>width</u> of E. coli bacteria varies within a range.
- <u>Plants</u> — e.g. a <u>tree</u> can have any <u>number of leaves</u> within a range.

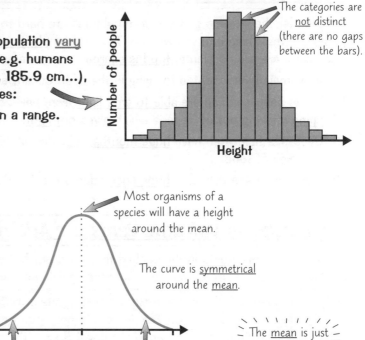

The categories are <u>not</u> distinct (there are no gaps between the bars).

A graph of continuous variation is an example of a <u>normal distribution curve</u> (a bell-shaped curve).

This isn't too scary — it just means that if you draw a <u>line graph</u> of your data you get a nice <u>symmetrical curve</u>.

Here's that height example again: ▬▶

Most organisms of a species will have a height around the mean.

The curve is <u>symmetrical</u> around the <u>mean</u>.

The <u>mean</u> is just an <u>average</u>.

Not many organisms will be a long way away from the mean height.

...or Discontinuous

<u>Discontinuous variation</u> is when there are <u>two or more distinct categories</u> — each individual falls into <u>only one</u> of these categories, there are <u>no intermediates</u>. Here are some examples:

- <u>Animals</u> — e.g. <u>humans</u> can only be <u>blood group</u> A, B, AB or O.
- <u>Microorganisms</u> — e.g. <u>bacteria</u> are either <u>antibiotic-resistant</u> or not.
- <u>Plants</u> — e.g. the <u>colour</u> of a <u>courgette</u> is either yellow, dark green or light green.

Four distinct blood groups

You Can Do a Practical to Show Variation

<u>Continuous</u> and <u>discontinuous</u> variation is easy to investigate in a group of people e.g. <u>your class</u>.

Continuous Variation

Record the <u>hand span</u> of everyone in your class (to find it, spread out your hand and measure the distance from the tip of the little finger to the tip of the thumb). You'll get a <u>range of data</u>, so you can draw a graph like the blue one above.

Discontinuous Variation

Record the <u>eye colour</u> of everyone in your class. You'll get data in <u>distinct categories</u> such as blue, brown etc. So you can draw a graph like the red one above.

My favourite blood group is AB B A...*

If you can't remember the difference between continuous and discontinuous just think of test results — e.g. if some results vary from 0% to 65.4% to 100% and anything in between, then they're <u>continuous</u>. But if some results are just pass or fail, they're <u>discontinuous</u>. Hope that helps you to pass your tests.

*Ask your mum.

Extreme Environments

Organisms which live in extreme environments like deserts or deep oceans need to be <u>specially adapted</u>.

Some Organisms Have Adapted to Living in the Deep Sea

Deep under the surface of the sea, conditions are hard to live in. There's virtually <u>no light</u> (sunlight can't penetrate that deep into the water). That means <u>plants can't grow</u> because they can't photosynthesise. Because there are no plants, <u>food is scarce</u> — organisms survive on scraps that sink down from above.

Some animals have adapted to living in the deep ocean, e.g.

1) Some deep-sea fish are <u>able to emit light</u> from parts of their body. E.g. the angler fish has a rod-shaped <u>spine</u> sticking out of its face which <u>gives out light</u>. The light <u>attracts prey</u>, which the angler fish then eats.

2) Deep-sea fish often have <u>huge mouths</u>, e.g. the rat-tail fish which moves along the seabed scooping up particles of food.

3) Many deep-sea fish have <u>huge eyes</u> adapted to the dark, and <u>long feelers</u> to help them locate prey.

Organisms in Volcanic Vents are Adapted to High Temperatures

There are <u>volcanic vents</u> in the <u>seabed</u> that send out hot water and minerals into the cold ocean. Some organisms have adapted to living around them.

Volcanic vents are also called hydrothermal vents.

1) The chemicals from the vents support <u>bacteria</u> that are able to make their own <u>food</u> using <u>chemical energy</u>. This is called <u>chemosynthesis</u>. It's a bit like photosynthesis, but (because there's hardly any light down there) it uses chemical energy instead of light energy.

2) These bacteria are at the bottom of a <u>food web</u> (they're producers) — animals feed on the bacteria.

3) The conditions are <u>extremely hot</u> and under <u>high pressure</u>. The bacteria which live near the vents must be specially <u>adapted</u> to cope with the high temperature and pressure.

Organisms in Polar Regions Have Adapted to the Cold

The <u>polar regions</u> are the Arctic and Antarctic — these places are <u>really cold</u>.
Some animals have adapted to living in these conditions e.g:

POLAR BEARS (in the arctic)

1) Polar bears have a <u>compact</u> (rounded) shape, which gives them a small <u>surface area</u> compared to <u>volume</u> — this <u>reduces heat loss</u>.

2) They have a thick layer of <u>blubber</u> for <u>insulation</u> — this also acts as an <u>energy store</u> when food is scarce.

3) Their <u>thick hairy coats</u> trap <u>a layer of warm air</u> next to the skin, and their <u>greasy fur</u> sheds water (this <u>prevents cooling</u> due to evaporation).

4) Their <u>big feet</u> help by <u>spreading their weight</u> — which stops them sinking into the snow or breaking thin ice.

5) Polar bears have <u>white fur</u> to match their surroundings — for <u>camouflage</u>.

PENGUINS (in the antarctic)

1) Penguins have similar adaptations to polar bears, such as a thick layer of <u>insulating fat</u> and <u>oily feathers</u> to shed water, which <u>reduce heat loss</u>.

2) They also <u>huddle together</u> in groups to <u>conserve heat</u>.

3) Penguins have a <u>streamlined</u> body to <u>reduce water resistance</u> — so they can <u>swim fast</u> to <u>catch fish</u>.

Zebras — adapted for hiding in front of railings...

You could go to the most horrible, dry, desolate, smelly, freezing, airless place in the world, and there would still be some <u>well-adapted little critter</u> able to live there. Take my house for example — it's freezing since the boiler broke, but I've adapted (if an extra jumper counts).

Natural Selection and Evidence for Evolution

There are always more organisms born than can survive, so they end up <u>competing</u> for stuff like food. Only the <u>fittest</u> survive, and they will <u>pass on</u> their characteristics to their offspring.

Natural Selection Means "Survival of the Fittest"

<u>Evolution</u> is the <u>slow and continuous change</u> of organisms from one generation to the next.
<u>Charles Darwin</u> came up with the <u>theory of natural selection</u> to <u>explain how</u> evolution occurs. It works like this:

1) Individuals are not all the same because of differences in their genes.
   So there is <u>variation</u> (see page 10) within populations of organisms.

2) Most organisms give birth to <u>more young</u> than can <u>survive</u> to adulthood.

3) But populations <u>don't</u> generally <u>increase quickly in size</u> because individuals have to <u>compete</u> with each other for <u>resources</u> that are in <u>limited supply</u> (e.g. food, water, mates, etc).

4) Those individuals with characteristics that make them <u>better adapted</u> to the environment have a <u>better chance of survival</u> and so are more likely to <u>breed</u> successfully.

5) So, the <u>genes</u> that are responsible for the useful characteristics are more likely to be <u>passed on</u> to the <u>next generation</u>.

6) However, some individuals will be <u>less well adapted</u> to their environment and may be less able to compete. These individuals are <u>less likely</u> to survive and reproduce.

7) <u>Over time</u>, there will be a higher proportion of individuals with <u>beneficial characteristics</u> — compared to those with <u>poorly adapted characteristics</u>. Eventually the poorly adapted characteristics may be <u>lost</u>.

There's Evidence to Support Evolution:

❶ DNA Research

1) The theory of evolution suggests that all organisms have evolved from <u>shared common ancestors</u>.

2) Closely related species <u>diverged</u> (evolved to become different species) more <u>recently</u>.

3) Evolution is caused by <u>gradual changes</u> in DNA.

4) So, organisms that diverged away from each other more <u>recently</u> should have more <u>similar DNA</u>. This is exactly what scientists found, e.g. <u>humans</u> and <u>chimps</u> have similar DNA.

❷ Resistant Organisms

1) The poison <u>warfarin</u> was used to <u>kill rats</u>.

2) But a certain gene gives rats <u>resistance</u> to warfarin — these rats are more likely to <u>survive</u> and <u>breed</u>.

3) So now there are rat populations that are <u>warfarin-resistant</u>.

The Scientific Community Validates Evidence About Evolution

1) The <u>scientific community</u> is all the scientists around the world, e.g. researchers, technicians and professors.

2) Scientists within the scientific community <u>accept</u> the theory of evolution because they've <u>shared</u> and <u>discussed</u> the <u>evidence</u> to make sure it's <u>valid</u> and <u>reliable</u>. There are three main ways they do this:

> Scientists publish their work in <u>SCIENTIFIC JOURNALS</u> (academic magazines). If other scientists can repeat the experiments using the same methods and get the <u>same results</u>, the scientific community can be pretty confident that the evidence is <u>reliable</u>.

> Before scientists can publish their work it has to undergo <u>PEER REVIEW</u>. This is when other scientists (peers) read and review the work, to check it's <u>valid</u> and that experiments are carried out to the <u>highest possible standards</u>.

> <u>SCIENTIFIC CONFERENCES</u> are <u>meetings</u> that scientists attend to <u>present</u> and <u>discuss</u> their work. They're an easy way for the latest hypotheses and evidence to be <u>shared</u> and <u>discussed</u>.

Natural selection... sounds like vegan chocolates...

Natural selection's all about the organisms with the <u>best characteristics</u> surviving to <u>pass on their genes</u> so that the whole species ends up <u>adapted</u> to its environment. It doesn't happen overnight though.

Speciation and Genes

First up, <u>speciation</u> — where evolution can lead to <u>new species</u>. Then you need to get to grips with <u>genes</u>...

Speciation is the Development of a New Species

<u>Speciation</u> occurs when <u>populations</u> of the <u>same species</u> become so <u>different</u> that they can <u>no longer breed</u> together to produce <u>fertile offspring</u>. It works like this:

① <u>Isolation</u> is where <u>populations</u> of a species are <u>separated</u>. This can happen due to a <u>physical barrier</u>. E.g. floods and earthquakes can cause barriers that <u>geographically isolate</u> some individuals from the main population.

② <u>Conditions</u> on either side of the barrier will be <u>slightly different</u>, e.g. they may have <u>different climates</u>. Because the environment is <u>different</u> on each side, <u>different characteristics</u> will become more common in each population due to <u>natural selection</u> (see page 13).

③ Eventually, individuals from the different populations will have <u>changed</u> so much that they <u>won't</u> be able to <u>breed</u> with one another to produce fertile offspring. The two groups will have become <u>separate species</u>.

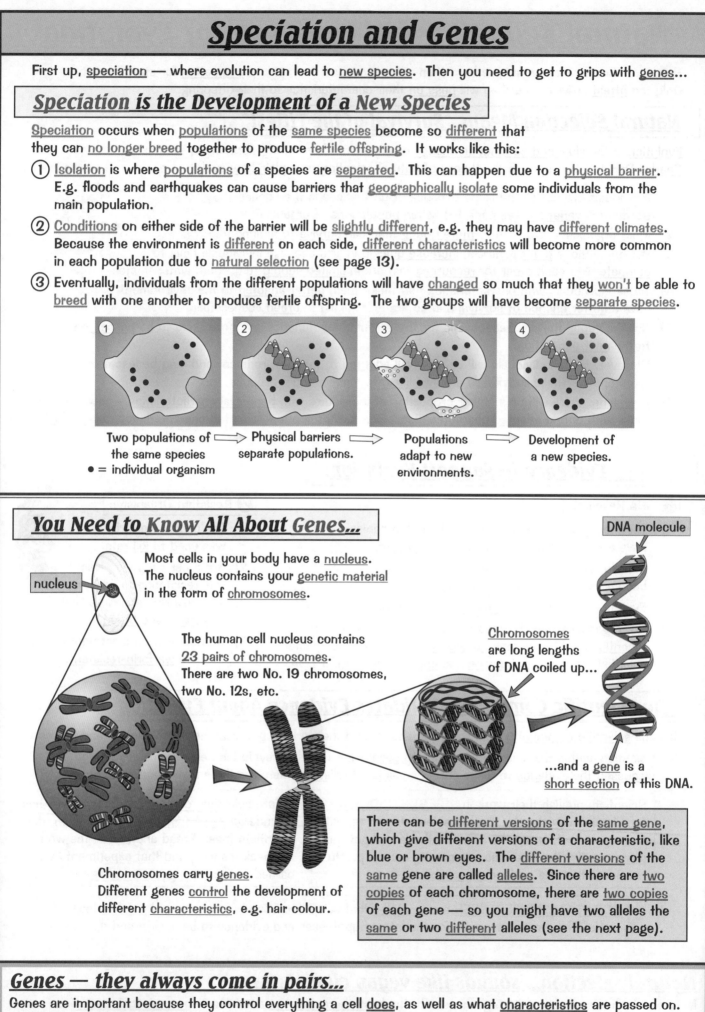

Two populations of the same species ⇒ Physical barriers separate populations. ⇒ Populations adapt to new environments. ⇒ Development of a new species.

● = individual organism

You Need to Know All About Genes...

DNA molecule

nucleus

Most cells in your body have a <u>nucleus</u>. The nucleus contains your <u>genetic material</u> in the form of <u>chromosomes</u>.

The human cell nucleus contains <u>23 pairs of chromosomes</u>. There are two No. 19 chromosomes, two No. 12s, etc.

<u>Chromosomes</u> are long lengths of DNA coiled up...

...and a <u>gene</u> is a <u>short section</u> of this DNA.

Chromosomes carry <u>genes</u>. Different genes <u>control</u> the development of different <u>characteristics</u>, e.g. hair colour.

There can be <u>different versions</u> of the <u>same gene</u>, which give different versions of a characteristic, like blue or brown eyes. The <u>different versions</u> of the <u>same</u> gene are called <u>alleles</u>. Since there are <u>two copies</u> of each chromosome, there are <u>two copies</u> of each gene — so you might have two alleles the <u>same</u> or two <u>different</u> alleles (see the next page).

Genes — they always come in pairs...

Genes are important because they control everything a cell <u>does</u>, as well as what <u>characteristics</u> are passed on. Make sure you really know your stuff 'cos you're going to hear a lot more about genes over the next few pages...

Genetic Diagrams

In genetics you're never more than a stone's throw away from a genetic diagram...

Genetic Diagrams Show the Possible Genes of Offspring

First of all, make sure you remember what an allele is from the previous page.
Then you need to learn these basics (otherwise it's hard to follow what's going on).

Remember, gametes (sperm or egg cells) only have one allele, but all the other cells in an organism have two.

1) In genetic diagrams letters are usually used to represent alleles.

2) If an organism has two alleles for a particular gene the same, then it's homozygous.
   If its two alleles for a particular gene are different, then it's heterozygous.

3) If the two alleles are different, only one can determine what characteristic is present. The allele for the characteristic that's shown is called the dominant allele (use a capital letter for dominant alleles — e.g. 'C'). The other one is called recessive (and you show these with small letters — e.g. 'c').

4) For an organism to display a recessive characteristic, both its alleles must be recessive (e.g. cc). But to display a dominant characteristic the organism can be either CC or Cc, because the dominant allele overrules the recessive one if the plant/animal/other organism is heterozygous.

Suppose You Find Yourself Cross-Breeding Crazy Hamsters...

Let's say that the gene which causes the crazy nature is recessive, so we use a small "h" for it, whilst normal (boring) behaviour is due to a dominant gene, so we represent it with a capital "H".

1) A crazy hamster must have the genotype hh. However, a normal hamster could have two possible genotypes — HH or Hh.

Genotype means what alleles you have. Phenotype means the actual characteristic.

2) Here's what happens if you breed from two homozygous hamsters:

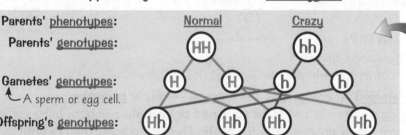

Parents' phenotypes:	Normal		Crazy	
Parents' genotypes:	(HH)		(hh)	
Gametes' genotypes:	(H) (H)		(h) (h)	
Offspring's genotypes:	(Hh)	(Hh)	(Hh)	(Hh)
Offspring's phenotypes:	All the offspring are normal (boring).			

↳ A sperm or egg cell.

If you don't like that diagram you can also do it like this:

Gametes' genotypes →
H | h
Hh | h
Hh | Hh
Hh

Offspring's genotypes

3) If two of these offspring now breed, you'll get the next generation:

Parents' phenotypes:	Normal		Normal	
Parents' genotypes:	(Hh)		(Hh)	
Gametes' genotypes:	(H) (h)		(H) (h)	
Offspring's genotypes:	(HH)	(Hh)	(hH)	(hh)
Offspring's phenotypes:	Normal	Normal	Normal	Crazy!

When you cross two parents to look at just one characteristic, it's called a monohybrid cross.

4) This gives a 3:1 ratio of normal to crazy offspring in this generation.
   Remember that "results" like this are only probabilities — they don't say definitely what'll happen.
   (most likely, you'll end up trying to contain a mini-riot of nine lunatic baby hamsters.)

What do you get if you cross a kangaroo and a sheep...

...a ratio of 1:1 kangsheep to sheeparoos... bet you thought I was going to say a woolly jumper.
In the exam you might be given the results of a breeding experiment and asked to say whether a characteristic is dominant or recessive. To figure it out, look at the ratios of the characteristic in different generations — just like in the diagrams. And remember that a 3:1 ratio of normal:crazy gives a 1 in 4 or 25% probability of being crazy.

Genetic Diagrams and Disorders

Usually we don't notice our genes — they all quietly bumble away, making proteins.
But a <u>faulty allele</u> (that makes a faulty protein) can cause a <u>genetic disorder</u>.

Cystic Fibrosis *is Caused by a Recessive Allele*

<u>Cystic fibrosis</u> is a <u>genetic disorder</u> of the <u>cell membranes</u>. It <u>results</u> in the body producing a lot of thick sticky <u>mucus</u> in the <u>air passages</u>, <u>gut</u> and <u>pancreas</u>. Symptoms include <u>breathing difficulties</u>, <u>lung infections</u>, <u>malnutrition</u> and <u>fertility problems</u>.

1) The allele which causes cystic fibrosis is a <u>recessive allele</u>, 'f', carried by about <u>1 person in 30</u>.

2) Because it's recessive, people with only <u>one copy</u> of the allele <u>won't</u> have the disorder — they're known as <u>carriers</u>.

3) For a child to have a chance of inheriting the disorder, <u>both parents</u> must be either <u>carriers</u> or <u>sufferers</u>.

4) As the diagram shows there's a <u>1 in 4 chance</u> of a child having the disorder if <u>both</u> parents are <u>carriers</u>.

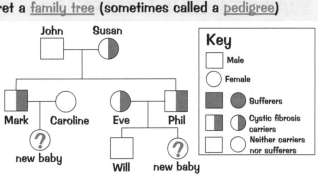

Knowing how inheritance works can help you to interpret a <u>family tree</u> (sometimes called a <u>pedigree</u>) — this is one for <u>cystic fibrosis</u>.

1) From the family tree, you can tell that the allele for cystic fibrosis <u>isn't</u> dominant because plenty of the family <u>carry</u> the allele but <u>aren't sufferers</u>.

2) There is a <u>0%</u> chance that Mark and Caroline's new baby will be a sufferer (ff) because Caroline is normal (FF).

3) There is a <u>25%</u> chance that Eve and Phil's new baby will be a sufferer and a <u>50%</u> chance that it will be a carrier (Ff) because both of its parents are carriers but not sufferers.

4) Many <u>genetic disorders</u> can be <u>detected</u> by analysing a cell's <u>genes</u> — this is <u>screening</u>. Family trees can help people <u>decide</u> whether or not to be screened or have their unborn baby screened. E.g. Eve and Phil may want to screen their unborn baby for <u>cystic fibrosis</u> because they're both carriers.

Sickle Cell Anaemia *is Also Caused by a Recessive Allele*

1) Sickle-cell anaemia is a <u>genetic disorder</u> characterised by funny-shaped red blood cells.

2) These red blood cells can get <u>stuck</u> in the capillaries, which <u>deprives</u> body cells of <u>oxygen</u>.

3) <u>Symptoms</u> include tiredness, painful joints and muscles, fever and anaemia.

4) It's caused by inheriting two <u>recessive</u> alleles 'a' (for anaemia). The normal allele is represented by an 'A'.

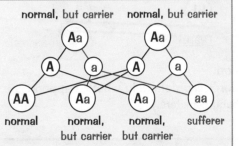

- If two people who <u>carry</u> the sickle cell anaemia allele have children, the <u>probability</u> of each child suffering from the disorder is 1 in 4 — <u>25%</u>.

- The ratio you'd expect in the children is <u>3:1</u>, non-sufferer:sufferer.

- If you see this ratio in the offspring you know <u>both</u> parents must have the <u>two different alleles</u>.

- Be careful with this one — it may be disguised as a <u>1:2:1</u> ratio (normal:carrier:sufferer), but it means the same thing.

Unintentional mooning — caused by faulty jeans...

We <u>all</u> have defective genes in us somewhere — but usually they don't cause a problem (as they're often <u>recessive</u>, and so if you have a healthy <u>dominant</u> allele too, you'll be fine).

Revision Summary for B1 Topic 1

Gee, all that business about all those topics — and it's all pretty serious stuff. It takes a real effort to get your head round it all. There are too many big fancy words, for one thing. But there you go — life's tough and you've just gotta face up to it. Use these questions to find out what you know — and what you don't. Then look back and learn the bits you didn't know. Then try the questions again, and again...

1) Briefly describe characteristics of organisms in the animal kingdom.
2) What main characteristic do organisms in the Chordata phylum have in common?
3) What do all vertebrates have in common?
4) What does oviparous mean? Name a group of vertebrates that are oviparous.
5) What is a species?
6) What is the name for the offspring of two different species?
7) In the binomial system each organism is given a two-part name. What does each part refer to?
8)* Devise a key to tell apart a worm, a snail, a centipede and a spider.
9) Other than the environment, what causes variation?
10) List three features of animals which aren't affected at all by environment, and three which are.
11) What is: a) continuous variation?
               b) discontinuous variation?
12) Give an example of a feature in humans where there is: a) continuous variation.
                                                            b) discontinuous variation.
13) Explain two ways that deep-sea fish have adapted to their habitat.
14) Explain two ways that polar bears are adapted to living in polar regions.
15) Explain Darwin's theory of natural selection.
16) Give three ways that the scientific community validate evidence.
17) What is speciation? Explain how geographical isolation can lead to speciation.
18) Draw a set of diagrams showing the relationship between: cell, nucleus, chromosomes, genes, DNA.
19) How many pairs of chromosomes are there in a normal human cell nucleus?
20) What is an allele?
21) What is meant by an organism being heterozygous? What about homozygous?
22) Describe the basic difference between a recessive allele and a dominant one.
23)*White colour in a plant is carried on a recessive allele, b. The dominant allele, B, gives blue flowers.
    After a cross between two plants, all the flowers of the second generation are blue. These are bred
    together and the result in the third generation is a ratio of 54 blue : 19 white flowers.
    What were the alleles of the flowers in the first generation?
24) What are the symptoms of cystic fibrosis?
25) Cystic fibrosis is caused by a recessive allele.
    If both parents are carriers, what is the probability of their child:a) being a carrier?
                                                                        b) suffering from the disorder?
26) Give two symptoms of sickle-cell anaemia.
27) Is the allele for sickle-cell anaemia dominant or recessive?

*Answers to these questions are given on p.108

Homeostasis

Homeostasis means <u>maintaining</u> the right <u>conditions</u> inside your body, so that everything <u>works properly</u>. Ace.

Homeostasis *is Maintaining a Stable Internal Environment*

Conditions in your body need to be kept <u>steady</u> so that cells can function properly. For example...

1) <u>Osmoregulation</u> (regulating <u>water</u> content) — you need to keep a balance between the water you gain (in drink, food, and from respiration) and the water you pee, sweat and breathe out.

2) <u>Thermoregulation</u> (regulating <u>body temperature</u>) — you need to get rid of <u>excess</u> body heat when you're hot, but <u>retain</u> heat when the environment is cold. See below for how your body does this.

3) <u>Blood glucose</u> regulation — you need to keep the glucose in your blood at a <u>steady level</u> (see p.22).

A mechanism called <u>negative feedback</u> helps to keep all these things steady:

- Changes in the environment trigger a response that <u>counteracts</u> the changes — e.g. a <u>rise</u> in body temperature causes a response that <u>lowers body temperature</u>.

- This means that the <u>internal environment</u> tends to stay around a <u>norm</u>, the level at which the cells work best.

- This only works within <u>certain limits</u> — if the environment changes too much then it might not be possible to <u>counteract</u> it.

(graph: body temperature vs time — increase from normal detected, response counteracts the increase, normal level, decrease from normal detected, response counteracts the decrease)

Body Temperature *is Controlled by the* Hypothalamus

All <u>enzymes</u> work best at a <u>certain temperature</u>. The enzymes in the human body work best at about <u>37 °C</u>.

1) There's a part of your brain called the <u>hypothalamus</u> that acts as your own <u>personal thermostat</u>.

2) It contains <u>receptors</u> that are sensitive to the <u>blood temperature</u> in the brain. It also receives impulses from receptors in the <u>skin</u> (nerve endings) that provide information about <u>skin temperature</u>.

3) When the hypothalamus detects a change, it causes a <u>response</u> in the <u>dermis</u> (deep layer of the skin):

When temperature receptors detect you're **TOO HOT:**	And when they detect you're **TOO COLD:**
1) <u>Erector muscles</u> relax, so <u>hairs</u> lie flat.	1) <u>Erector muscles</u> contract. <u>Hairs</u> stand on end to trap an insulating layer of air, which helps keep you warm.
2) <u>Lots of sweat</u> (containing <u>water</u> and <u>salts</u>) is produced. When the sweat <u>evaporates</u> it <u>transfers heat</u> from your skin to the environment, cooling you down.	2) <u>Very little sweat</u> is produced.
3) <u>Blood vessels</u> close to the surface of the skin <u>dilate</u> (widen). This is called <u>vasodilation</u>. It allows <u>more blood</u> to flow near the <u>surface</u>, so it can <u>transfer more heat</u> into the <u>surroundings</u>.	3) Blood vessels near the surface of the skin <u>constrict</u> (<u>vasoconstriction</u>). This means <u>less blood</u> flows near the surface, so <u>less heat</u> is transferred to the surroundings.

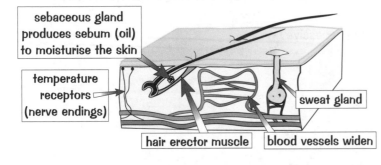

sebaceous gland produces sebum (oil) to moisturise the skin

temperature receptors (nerve endings)

sweat gland

hair erector muscle   blood vessels widen

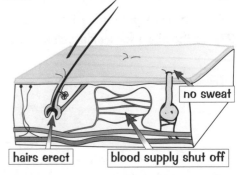

no sweat

hairs erect   blood supply shut off

Learn about homeostasis — and keep your cool...

Homeostasis means 'maintaining a <u>stable internal environment</u>'. Say this 20 times and recite it in your sleep. As well as keeping your <u>temperature</u> right, it's also about keeping <u>water</u> and <u>sugar</u> at the right level. Lovely jubbly.

Hormones and Nerves

There are two ways that signals can be sent from one part of the body to another — using slooow <u>hormones</u> or quick quick quick <u>nerves</u>. And guess what, you have to know about them <u>both</u>. Enjoy. You're welcome.

Hormones are Chemical Messengers Sent in the Blood

1) Hormones are chemicals produced in various <u>glands</u> (called <u>endocrine</u> glands).

2) They are released directly into the <u>blood</u>. The blood then carries them to other parts of the body.

3) They travel all over the body but they only affect <u>particular cells</u> in particular places.

4) The affected cells are called <u>target cells</u> — they have the right <u>receptors</u> to respond to that hormone. An organ that contains target cells is called a <u>target organ</u>.

5) Hormones travel at "<u>the speed of blood</u>".

6) They have <u>long-lasting effects</u>.

> **Learn this definition:**
> Hormones ...are <u>chemical</u> <u>messengers</u> which <u>travel in the</u> <u>blood</u> to <u>activate target cells</u>.

Neurones Transmit Information Around the Body

<u>Neurones</u> (nerve cells) transmit information as <u>electrical impulses</u> around the body.

1) Neurones have <u>branched endings</u> called <u>dendrons</u>, so they can <u>connect</u> with lots of other neurones.

2) The electrical impulse is passed along the <u>axon</u> of the cell.

3) There's a <u>myelin sheath</u> along the axon that acts as an <u>electrical insulator</u>, which stops the impulse getting <u>lost</u>. It also <u>speeds</u> up the electrical impulse.

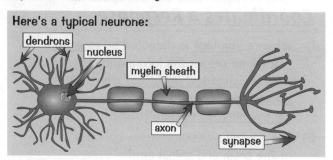

Here's a typical neurone:
dendrons — nucleus — myelin sheath — axon — synapse

4) Neurones are <u>long</u>, which also <u>speeds up</u> the impulse (<u>connecting</u> with <u>another neurone</u> slows the impulse down, so one long neurone is much <u>quicker</u> than lots of short ones joined together).

5) The <u>connection</u> between <u>two neurones</u> is called a <u>synapse</u>. It's basically just a very tiny gap:

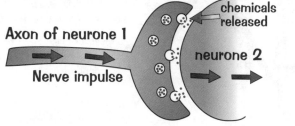

Axon of neurone 1
Nerve impulse
chemicals released
neurone 2

• The nerve impulse is transmitted by chemicals called <u>neurotransmitters</u>, which <u>diffuse</u> across the gap.

• The neurotransmitters then set off a <u>new electrical</u> <u>impulse</u> in the <u>next neurone</u>.

Hormones and Nerves Do Similar Jobs — but There are Differences

Nerves
1) Very <u>FAST</u> message.
2) Act for a very <u>SHORT TIME</u>.
3) Act on a very <u>PRECISE AREA</u>.
4) <u>ELECTRICAL</u> message.

Hormones
1) <u>SLOWER</u> message.
2) Act for a <u>LONG TIME</u>.
3) Act in a more <u>GENERAL</u> way.
4) <u>CHEMICAL</u> message.

Laughing at a funny joke releases stress-relieving hormones...

What's red and sits in the corner... A naughty strawberry. So now you're fully destressed, listen up... Hormones control various <u>organs</u> and <u>cells</u> in the body, though they tend to control things that aren't <u>immediately</u> life-threatening. They're not as quick as using neurones, but their effects can last much <u>longer</u>.

The Nervous System

The <u>nervous system</u> is what lets you <u>react</u> to what goes on around you, so you'd find life tough without it.

Sense Organs Detect Stimuli

A <u>stimulus</u> is a <u>change in your environment</u> that you may need to react to (e.g. a grizzly bear looking hungrily at you). You need to be constantly monitoring what's going on so you can respond if you need to.

1) You have five different <u>sense organs</u> — <u>eyes</u>, <u>ears</u>, <u>nose</u>, <u>tongue</u> and <u>skin</u>.

2) They all contain different <u>receptors</u>. Receptors are groups of cells which are <u>sensitive</u> to a <u>stimulus</u>. They change <u>stimulus energy</u> (e.g. light energy) into <u>electrical impulses</u>.

3) A stimulus can be <u>light</u>, <u>sound</u>, <u>touch</u>, <u>pressure</u>, <u>chemical</u>, or a change in <u>position</u> or <u>temperature</u>.

The Five Sense Organs and the receptors that each contains:

1) **Eyes**   <u>Light</u> receptors.

2) **Ears**   <u>Sound</u> and "<u>balance</u>" receptors.

3) **Nose**   <u>Smell</u> receptors — sensitive to chemical stimuli.

4) **Tongue**   <u>Taste</u> receptors — sensitive to bitter, salt, sweet, sour and savoury (these are all chemical stimuli).

5) **Skin** Sensitive to <u>touch</u> (<u>pressure</u>) and <u>temperature change</u>.

The Central Nervous System Coordinates a Response

1) When a <u>stimulus</u> is detected by <u>receptors</u> in a sense organ, the information is sent (as <u>electrical impulses</u>) along <u>sensory neurones</u> to the <u>central nervous system</u> (CNS).

2) The central nervous system consists of <u>the brain</u> and <u>spinal cord</u>.

3) The CNS <u>coordinates</u> the response (in other words, it <u>decides what to do</u> about the stimulus and tells something to do it).

4) The CNS then sends information to an <u>effector</u> (<u>muscle</u> or <u>gland</u>) along a <u>motor neurone</u>. The effector then <u>responds</u> accordingly.

Sensory Neurones

<u>Long dendrons</u> and short axons carry nerve impulses from the <u>receptors</u> in the sense organs to the <u>CNS</u>.

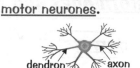
receptor cells
dendron   axon

Relay Neurones

<u>Many short dendrons and axons</u> carry nerve impulses from <u>sensory neurones</u> to <u>motor neurones</u>.

dendron   axon

Effectors

Muscles and glands are known as <u>effectors</u> — they respond in different ways. <u>Muscles contract</u> in response to a nervous impulse, whereas <u>glands secrete substances</u>, e.g. hormones.

Motor Neurones

<u>Many short dendrons</u> and one long axon carry nerve impulses from the CNS to the <u>effectors</u> (muscle or gland).

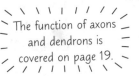
dendron   axon   effector cells

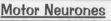
The function of axons and dendrons is covered on page 19.

Your tongue's evolved for Chinese meals — sweet, sour, MSG...

I'm so kind, I've just spent a whole hour thinking of how you could remember the <u>order</u> of a <u>coordinated response</u>: <u>s</u>timulus, <u>r</u>eceptor, <u>s</u>ensory neurone, <u>CNS</u>, <u>m</u>otor <u>n</u>eurone, <u>e</u>ffector, <u>r</u>esponse. Ready? <u>S</u>ofa, <u>r</u>emote, <u>s</u>earch for <u>N</u>eighbours, <u>c</u>hoose 'Neighbours series', <u>m</u>ental <u>n</u>ote when it's on, <u>e</u>asy — <u>r</u>ecord it.

Investigating Stimuli and Reflexes

If you were to unfold your brain and lie it out flat, it would cover an ironing board. Apparently.*

You can Carry Out a Practical to Investigate External Stimuli

For example, you can investigate skin sensitivity like this:

1) In pairs, one person wears a blindfold, or promises not to look.

2) The other person uses a hairpin (or a paperclip) with the 2 points a fixed distance apart (e.g. start at 3 mm) to touch an area of the blindfolded person's skin (e.g their elbow).

3) The blindfolded person is then asked how many points they can feel.

4) If the blindfolded person only feels one point, the experiment is repeated with the points further apart until they feel two points. The distance at which they feel two points is recorded.

5) This is repeated for different areas of skin (e.g. toes, fingers).

6) On really sensitive places, like the fingers or lips, the blindfolded person will feel both points when they're a short distance apart. This is because sensitive areas have lots of touch receptors.

7) But on less sensitive areas, like the elbow, they'll only feel both points when they're much further apart, because these areas have fewer touch receptors.

Remember, you need to control any other variables that could affect the results, e.g. the type of pin that's used.

Reflexes Help Prevent Injury

1) Reflexes are automatic responses to certain stimuli — they can reduce the chances of being injured.

2) For example, if someone shines a bright light in your eyes, your pupils automatically get smaller so that less light gets into the eye — this stops it getting damaged.

3) The passage of information in a reflex (from receptor to effector) is called a reflex arc.

A Reflex Arc Goes Through the Central Nervous System

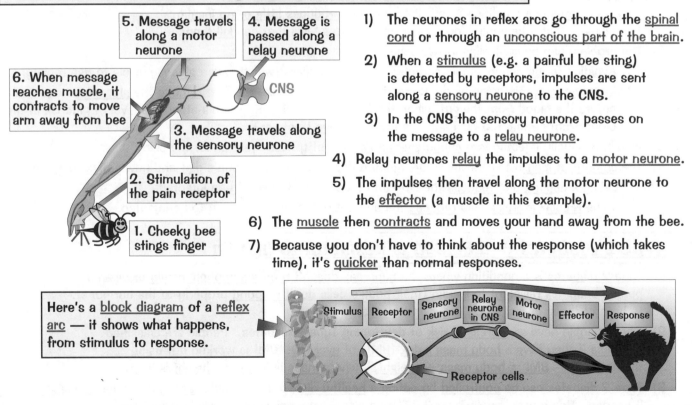

5. Message travels along a motor neurone

4. Message is passed along a relay neurone

CNS

6. When message reaches muscle, it contracts to move arm away from bee

3. Message travels along the sensory neurone

2. Stimulation of the pain receptor

1. Cheeky bee stings finger

1) The neurones in reflex arcs go through the spinal cord or through an unconscious part of the brain.

2) When a stimulus (e.g. a painful bee sting) is detected by receptors, impulses are sent along a sensory neurone to the CNS.

3) In the CNS the sensory neurone passes on the message to a relay neurone.

4) Relay neurones relay the impulses to a motor neurone.

5) The impulses then travel along the motor neurone to the effector (a muscle in this example).

6) The muscle then contracts and moves your hand away from the bee.

7) Because you don't have to think about the response (which takes time), it's quicker than normal responses.

Here's a block diagram of a reflex arc — it shows what happens, from stimulus to response.

Stimulus | Receptor | Sensory neurone | Relay neurone in CNS | Motor neurone | Effector | Response

Receptor cells

Don't get all twitchy — just learn it...

Listen up... GCSE Science isn't just a test of what you know, it's also a test of how well you can apply knowledge. So don't worry if you're asked about a different reflex — the reflex arc is the same, so just apply what you know.

Insulin and Diabetes

Blood glucose is controlled as part of homeostasis (see page 18), using the hormones insulin and glucagon.

Insulin and Glucagon Control Blood Sugar Level

1) Eating foods containing carbohydrate puts glucose (a type of sugar) into the blood from the gut.

2) The normal metabolism of cells removes glucose from the blood.

3) Vigorous exercise removes much more glucose from the blood.

4) To control the level of blood glucose there has to be a way to add or remove glucose from the blood...

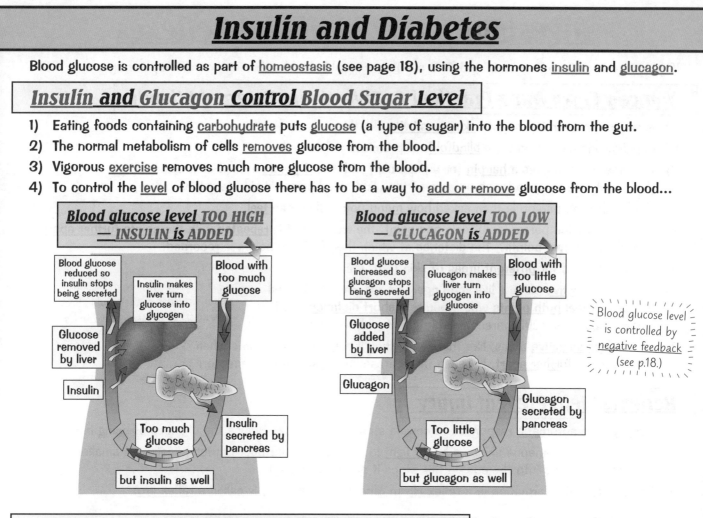

Blood glucose level is controlled by negative feedback (see p.18.)

Type 1 Diabetes — Caused by a Lack of Insulin

Remember, insulin reduces blood sugar level.

1) Type 1 diabetes is a condition where the pancreas produces little or no insulin. The result is that a person's blood sugar can rise to a level that can kill them.

2) The problem can be controlled in two ways:

   a) Avoiding foods rich in simple carbohydrates, i.e. sugars (which cause glucose levels to rise rapidly).

   b) Injecting insulin into the blood at mealtimes. This will make the liver remove the glucose as soon as it enters the blood from the gut, when the food is being digested. This stops the level of glucose in the blood from getting too high and is a very effective treatment.

3) Insulin is usually injected into subcutaneous tissue (fatty tissue just under the skin).

4) The amount of insulin that needs to be injected depends on the person's diet and how active they are, e.g.:

   • Eating a healthy diet reduces the amount of insulin that needs to be injected.

   • Doing regular exercise also reduces the amount of insulin that needs to be injected.

Type 2 Diabetes — a Person is Resistant to Insulin

1) Type 2 diabetes is a condition where the pancreas doesn't produce enough insulin or when a person becomes resistant to insulin (their body's cells don't respond properly to the hormone). In both of these cases, blood sugar level rises.

2) Obese people have an increased risk of developing Type 2 diabetes. People are classified as obese if they have a body mass index (BMI) of over 30. BMI is worked out using this formula — $BMI = body\ mass \div (height)^2$, where mass is in kg and height is in m.

3) Type 2 diabetes can be controlled by eating a healthy diet, getting regular exercise and losing weight if needed. Some people with Type 2 diabetes also have medication or insulin injections.

And people used to think the pancreas was just a cushion... *(true)*

So Type 2 diabetes is linked to obesity, but scientists are still researching exactly how they're linked.

Plant Growth Hormones

Plants have hormones too, you know. Not that you'll ever see one scoffing a chocolate bar on a bad day.

Plants Respond to Different Stimuli

1) Plants can respond to stimuli (e.g. light, gravity or moisture) by regulating their growth.

2) A plant's growth response is called a tropism. A positive tropism is growing towards a stimulus.

3) You need to know these two responses:

PHOTOTROPISM — the growth of a plant in response to light. Shoots are positively phototropic — they grow towards light.

GRAVITROPISM (GEOTROPISM) — the growth of a plant in response to gravity. Roots are positively gravitropic — they grow downwards.

4) Plant growth hormones, e.g. auxin and gibberellin, allow plants to grow in response to stimuli.

Auxin Stimulates Plant Tips to Grow

1) Auxin is a plant hormone that controls growth at the tips of shoots and roots.

2) Auxin is produced in the tips and diffuses backwards to stimulate the cells just behind the tips to elongate (grow longer).

3) If the tip of a shoot is removed, no auxin will be available and the shoot stops growing.

4) Auxin promotes growth in the shoot but high concentrations inhibit growth in the root — producing the desired result...

Auxin

SHOOTS ARE POSITIVELY PHOTOTROPIC

1) When a shoot tip is exposed to light, more auxin accumulates on the side that's in the shade than the side that's in the light.

2) This makes the cells grow (elongate) faster on the shaded side, so the shoot bends towards the light.

3) This response enables plants to absorb more light for photosynthesis. Photosynthesis provides sugar, which provides energy for growth.

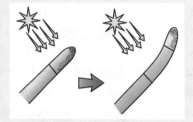

ROOTS ARE POSITIVELY GRAVITROPIC (GEOTROPIC)

1) When a root is growing sideways, gravity produces an unequal distribution of auxin in the tip, with more auxin on the lower side.

2) But in a root the extra auxin inhibits growth. This means the cells on top elongate faster, and the root bends downwards.

3) This response enables plants to extend their roots deep into the soil, so that they're well anchored. The plants can absorb more water and minerals, which are needed for photosynthesis.

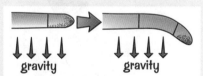

gravity   gravity

Gibberellin Stimulates Plant Stems to Grow

1) Gibberellin is another type of plant growth hormone.

2) It stimulates seed germination, stem growth and flowering.

3) It stimulates the stems of plants to grow by stem elongation — this helps plants to grow tall. If a dwarf variety of a plant is treated with gibberellin, it can grow to the same height as the tall variety.

4) Auxin and gibberellin can work together to have a really big effect on plant growth, e.g. together they help plants grow very tall.

What did the tall plant say to the short plant — you're talking gibberellish...

Who knew plants could be so hormonal... Not me for sure. The idea of plants having hormones might sound a trifle odd, but they make sure that plants grow in a useful direction, e.g. shoots grow towards light. Mmm, trifle.

Plant Growth Hormones — Experiments

You shouldn't just believe everything you read in Biology books, you know. They could tell you anything. But luckily for you, I always tell the truth — and here's some good old <u>classic plant experiments</u> to prove it.

You Need to be Able to Interpret Experimental Data on Plant Hormones

Take a look at these <u>two experiments</u>...

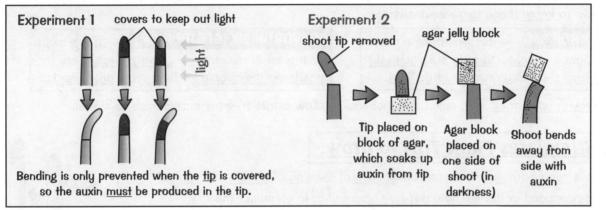

Experiment 1 — covers to keep out light — light

Bending is only prevented when the <u>tip</u> is covered, so the auxin <u>must</u> be produced in the tip.

Experiment 2 — shoot tip removed — agar jelly block

Tip placed on block of agar, which soaks up auxin from tip

Agar block placed on one side of shoot (in darkness)

Shoot bends away from side with auxin

...they show that auxin is <u>produced</u> in the <u>tip</u> of the plant (experiment 1) and causes <u>faster growth</u> on the side of the shoot where its <u>concentration</u> is <u>highest</u> (experiment 2). You need to be able to <u>interpret data</u> from experiments just like these — so make sure you know all about <u>auxin</u> and <u>gibberellin</u> from the previous page.

You can do a Practical to Investigate Plant Growth Responses

For example, you can investigate the effect of <u>light</u> on the <u>growth</u> of cress seeds like this...

1) Put <u>10 cress seeds</u> into three different Petri dishes, each lined with <u>moist filter paper</u>. (Remember to label your dishes, e.g. A, B, C.)

2) Shine a <u>light</u> onto one of the dishes from <u>above</u> and two of the dishes from <u>different directions</u> (see below).

3) Leave your poor little cress seeds alone for <u>one week</u>, what have they ever done to you...

4) ...until you can <u>observe</u> their <u>responses</u> — and hey presto, you'll find the seedlings <u>grow towards the light</u>.

Remember, these responses are controlled by auxin — see p.23

5) You know that the <u>growth response</u> of the cress seeds is due to <u>light</u> only, if you <u>control</u> all other variables.

Examples of variables that could <u>affect the experiment</u> and so need to be <u>controlled</u> are:

VARIABLE	HOW TO CONTROL IT
number of seeds	use the same number of seeds in each dish
type of seed	use seeds that all come from the same packet
temperature	use a thermometer to make sure the temperature of each dish is the same
water	use a measuring cylinder to add the same amount of water to each dish
light intensity	keep the distance between the bulb and dish the same for each dish

A plant auxin to a bar — 'ouch'...

...yeah I know, I know, but there's only so long I can cope with plant hormones before I go a bit doo-lally... So why not give yourself a break from my drivel — cover up the page, scribble down what you know, then see how much you got right. Anything you're not sure about, keep learning and learning till you know it.

Commercial Use of Plant Hormones

Plant hormones can be <u>extracted</u>, or <u>artificial versions</u> can be made. Then we can use them to do all kinds of useful things, including <u>killing weeds</u>, <u>growing cuttings</u>, <u>ripening fruit</u> and making <u>seedless fruit</u>.

1) As Selective Weedkillers

Unhappy weeds

1) Most <u>weeds</u> growing in fields of crops or in a lawn are <u>broad-leaved</u>, in contrast to <u>grasses</u> and <u>cereals</u> which have very <u>narrow leaves</u>.
2) <u>Selective weedkillers</u> have been developed from <u>plant growth hormones</u> which only affect the <u>broad-leaved plants</u>.
3) They totally <u>disrupt</u> their normal growth patterns, which soon <u>kills</u> them, whilst leaving the grass and crops <u>untouched</u>.

2) Growing from Cuttings with Rooting Powder

1) A <u>cutting</u> is part of a plant that has been <u>cut off it</u>, like the end of a branch with a few leaves on it.
2) Normally, if you stick cuttings in the soil they <u>won't grow</u>, but if you add <u>rooting powder</u>, which contains a plant <u>growth hormone</u>, they will <u>produce roots</u> rapidly and start growing as <u>new plants</u>.
3) This enables growers to produce lots of <u>clones</u> (exact copies) of a really good plant <u>very quickly</u>.

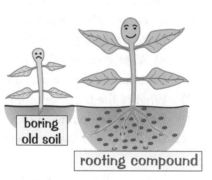

boring old soil

rooting compound

3) Controlling the Ripening of Fruit

1) The <u>ripening</u> of fruits can be controlled either while they are still on the plant, or during <u>transport</u> to the shops.
2) This allows the fruit to be picked while it's still <u>unripe</u> (and therefore firmer and <u>less easily damaged</u>).
3) <u>Ripening hormone</u> is then added and the fruit will ripen on the way to the supermarket and be <u>perfect</u> just as it reaches the shelves.

4) Producing Seedless Fruit

1) Fruit (with seeds in the middle) normally only grows on plants which have been <u>pollinated by insects</u>. If the plant <u>doesn't</u> get pollinated, the fruit and seeds <u>don't grow</u>.
2) If <u>growth hormones</u> are applied to the <u>unpollinated flowers</u> of some types of plant, the <u>fruit will grow</u> but the <u>seeds won't</u>. Some <u>seedless citrus fruits</u> can be grown this way.
3) <u>Hormones</u> are also used in the production of <u>seedless grapes</u> (although these are usually fertilised first).

Look, no pips...

You will ripen when I SAY you can ripen — and NOT BEFORE...

If you want some fruit to ripen, put them into a paper bag with a banana. The banana releases a ripening hormone called <u>ethene</u> which causes the fruit to ripen. Bad apples also release lots of ethene. Unfortunately, this means if you've got one bad apple in a barrel, you'll soon have lots of bad apples. See, every silver lining has a cloud.

Revision Summary for B1 Topic 2

This section covers everything you need to know about responding to change — homeostasis, nerves and hormones (including plant hormones). There's a lot to take in, so get yourself ready for some questions — they're the only way to find out if you really know your stuff. If the answers to these questions don't roll off your tongue immediately, I'm afraid you've got to go back to the page and relearn it. Here goes...

1) What is homeostasis?
2) Describe how body temperature is reduced when you're too hot.
3) Describe how body temperature is increased when you're too cold.
4) What are hormones?
5) How do hormones travel around the body?
6) What name is given to the chemicals found at synapses?
7) List the four main differences between nerves and hormones.
8) List the five sense organs and the receptors that each one contains.
9) a) What do the letters CNS stand for?
   b) What does the CNS consist of?
   c) What does the CNS do?
10) Describe an experiment you could do to investigate the sensitivity of different areas of skin.
11) What is the purpose of a reflex?
12) Describe the pathway of a reflex arc from stimulus to response.
13) Describe what happens when blood glucose level is: a) too high
                                                          b) too low.
14) Describe the main way in which Type 1 diabetes can be controlled.
15) What does it mean if a person is 'resistant to insulin'?
16)* Sophie is 1.5 m tall and weighs 58 kg. a) What is her BMI?   b) Is she obese?
17) What is the name given to a plant's growth response to light?
18) What is auxin?
19) Shoots are positively phototropic. What does this mean?
20) Roots are positively gravitropic. Explain the role of auxin in this response.
21) List three things that gibberellin stimulates in plants.
22) Describe an experiment you could do to show phototropism in cress seedlings.
23) Explain how plant hormones are used as selective weedkillers.
24) Give three other ways that plant growth hormones are used commercially.

*Answer to this question is given on p.108

Drugs

Drugs alter what goes on in your body. Your body's essentially a seething mass of chemical reactions — drugs can interfere with these reactions, sometimes for the better, sometimes not.

Drugs Can be Beneficial or Harmful

1) Most drugs are chemical substances that affect the central nervous system.
   They cause changes in psychological behaviour and can be addictive (see below).

2) Some drugs are medically useful, such as antibiotics (e.g. penicillin).
   But many drugs are dangerous if misused.

3) This is why you can buy some drugs over the counter at a pharmacy, but others are restricted so you can
   only get them on prescription — your doctor decides if you should have them.

4) Some people get addicted to drugs — this means they have a physical need for the drug,
   and if they don't get it they get withdrawal symptoms. It's not just illegal drugs
   that are addictive — many legal ones are as well, e.g. caffeine in coffee.
   Caffeine withdrawal symptoms include irritability and shaky hands.

5) Tolerance develops with some drugs — the body gets used to having it and so you need a higher dose to
   give the same effect. This can happen with both legal drugs (e.g. alcohol), and illegal drugs (e.g. heroin).

6) If someone's addicted to a drug but wants to get off it, rehabilitation can help — this is where you get help
   and support to try and overcome an addiction.

You Need to Know All About These Drugs...

1) Depressants — e.g. alcohol. These decrease the activity of the brain. This slows down the
   responses of the nervous system, causing slow reactions (see below) and poor judgement of
   speed and distances (which is why drink driving is dangerous).

2) Stimulants — e.g. nicotine, caffeine. These do the opposite of depressants — they increase
   the activity of the brain, by increasing the amount of neurotransmitter at some neurone synapses
   (see page 19). This increases the speed of reactions, and makes you feel more alert and awake.
   Stimulant drugs are often used to treat depression.

3) Painkillers — e.g. narcotics like morphine. These decrease the feeling of pain.
   Different painkillers work in different ways. E.g. morphine is a strong painkiller
   that works by blocking the nerve impulses in the brain.

4) Hallucinogens — e.g. LSD. They distort what's seen and heard
   by altering the pathways nerve impulses normally travel along.

Reaction Time is How Quickly You Respond

Reaction time is the time it takes to respond to a stimulus (often less than a second).
It can be affected by things like drugs. Reaction time can be measured like this...

1) One person holds a ruler vertically between the thumb and forefinger of
   a second person. They then let go without giving any warning.

2) The second person tries to catch the ruler as quickly as they can
   — as soon as they see it fall.

3) Reaction time is measured by how far down the ruler is caught
   — the further down, the slower their reactions.

30 cm

0 cm

A   B

Person A reacted
quicker than person B.

Person A beat person B at air hockey every time...

Make sure you learn the four different types of drug, and what they do, e.g. depressants slow down your reactions.
Tiredness slows down reaction times too — so make sure you get a good night's sleep before your exam...

Smoking, Alcohol and Organ Transplants

Everyone knows that drinking and smoking don't do you much good. However, some people can damage their organs so much that the only option is an organ transplant.

Smoking Tobacco Can Cause Quite a Few Problems

1) Tobacco smoke contains carbon monoxide — this combines irreversibly with haemoglobin in red blood cells, meaning the blood can carry less oxygen. In pregnant women, this can deprive the foetus of oxygen, leading to the baby being born underweight.

2) Tobacco smoke also contains carcinogens (chemicals that can lead to cancer), like tar. Lung cancer is way more common among smokers than non-smokers. It's estimated that 90% of lung cancers are associated with smoking (including passive smoking).

3) And to top it all off, smoking tobacco is addictive — because of the drug nicotine in tobacco smoke.

Alcohol Has Some Harmful Effects Too

Alcohol can affect a person straight away and in the future:

SHORT-TERM
1) Alcohol slows your reactions because it's a depressant (see page 27).
2) Being drunk leads to blurred vision and can also lower inhibitions — perhaps leading to people doing things they normally wouldn't.

LONG-TERM
1) Alcohol is poisonous. Normally, the liver breaks down the toxic alcohol into harmless by-products. But drinking too much too often causes the death of liver cells, forming scar tissue that starts to block blood flow through the liver — this is called cirrhosis. If the liver can't do its normal job of cleaning the blood, dangerous substances start to build up and damage the rest of the body.
2) Too much drinking can also lead to brain damage.

Organ Transplants Can Cure Diseases — But There Are Ethical Issues

If an organ's severely damaged (e.g. due to cirrhosis) it can be replaced by a donated natural organ.

1) Living donors can donate whole (or parts of) certain organs. For example, you can live with just one of your two kidneys and donate the other, or you can donate a piece of your liver.

2) Organs from people who have recently died, or who are brain dead, can also be transplanted.

3) But there's a big shortage of donors in the UK...

- You can join the NHS Organ Donor Register to show you're willing to donate organs after you die. However, doctors still need your family's consent before they can use the organs for a transplant.
- Some people say it should be made easier for doctors to use the organs of people who have died. One suggestion is to have an opt-out system instead — this means anyone's organs can be used unless the person has registered to say they don't want them to be donated.

4) Because of the organ shortage, some people may be less likely to get an organ transplant (e.g. if they are unlikely to survive the operation). Other people may only be considered if they change their lifestyle, e.g:

- Obese (very overweight) people can have a greater risk of dying after surgery, so they might have to lose weight before they are considered for organ transplants e.g. heart transplants.
- People who have damaged their liver through drinking too much alcohol might not be considered for liver transplants unless they stop drinking — more alcohol would damage their new liver.

5) Some people think that those who have harmed their own organs don't deserve an organ transplant as much as those people whose organs have been damaged through illness. But transplant guidelines aren't based on who would "deserve" a transplant, but who is most likely to benefit.

I think I need a brain transplant to learn all this lot...

In the exam you might have to evaluate data on smoking and its effects on health. So make sure you know the difference between correlation and cause (see page 5). A correlation doesn't always equal cause.

Infectious Diseases

An <u>infectious</u> disease is a disease that can be <u>transmitted</u> from one person to another (so obviously <u>not all</u> diseases are infectious). Sounds like it's going to be a cheery topic...

Infectious Diseases **are Caused by Pathogens**

1) <u>Pathogens</u> are <u>microorganisms</u> (microbes) that cause <u>disease</u>.
2) They include some <u>bacteria</u>, <u>protozoa</u> (certain single-celled creatures), <u>fungi</u> and all <u>viruses</u>.
3) Pathogens can <u>spread</u> in different ways:

Water	Some pathogens can be picked up by drinking or bathing in <u>dirty water</u>. E.g. <u>Cholera</u> is a <u>bacterial infection</u> that causes <u>diarrhoea</u> and <u>dehydration</u>. It's spread when <u>drinking water</u> is <u>contaminated</u> with the diarrhoea of other sufferers.
Food	Other pathogens are picked up by <u>eating contaminated food</u>. E.g. <u>Salmonella</u> bacteria cause <u>food poisoning</u> and are found in food that has been <u>kept too long</u> or <u>not cooked properly</u>.
Air	Airborne pathogens are carried in the air in <u>droplets</u> produced when you <u>cough</u> or <u>sneeze</u> — so other people can <u>breathe them in</u>. E.g. the <u>influenza virus</u> that causes <u>flu</u> is spread this way.
Contact	Some pathogens can be picked up by <u>touching</u> contaminated surfaces, including the <u>skin</u>. E.g. <u>athlete's foot</u> is a <u>fungus</u> which makes skin itch and flake off. It's most commonly spread by touching the same things as an infected person, e.g. <u>shower floors</u> and <u>towels</u>.
Body fluids	Some pathogens are spread by <u>body fluids</u> such as <u>blood</u> (e.g. by <u>sharing needles</u> to inject drugs), <u>breast milk</u> (through breast feeding) and <u>semen</u> (through sex). E.g. the <u>HIV</u> virus that causes <u>AIDS</u> (a disease which stops the <u>immune system</u> from working properly) is spread by body fluids.
Animal vectors	<u>Vectors</u> are animals that <u>spread disease</u>. Examples of vectors include: • <u>Anopheles mosquito</u> — it carries the <u>protozoan</u> that causes <u>malaria</u> (a disease that can damage the brain and kidneys or even be fatal). It spreads the disease by <u>biting</u> other organisms. • <u>House fly</u> — it carries the <u>bacterium</u> that causes <u>dysentery</u> (a disease that causes severe diarrhoea). It spreads the disease by carrying the bacteria onto <u>food</u>.

Physical **and Chemical Barriers Stop Pathogens Entering the Body**

You need to know about two different types of barrier against pathogens — <u>physical</u> and <u>chemical</u>.

PHYSICAL BARRIERS

1) The SKIN

<u>Undamaged skin</u> is a very effective barrier against microorganisms.
And if it gets <u>damaged</u>, blood <u>clots</u> quickly to <u>seal cuts</u> and keep microorganisms <u>out</u>.

2) The RESPIRATORY SYSTEM

The whole <u>respiratory tract</u> (nasal passage, trachea and lungs) is lined with <u>mucus</u> and <u>cilia</u>. The mucus catches <u>dust</u> and <u>bacteria</u> before they reach the lungs and the cilia push the gunk-filled mucus away from the lungs.

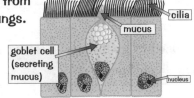

cilia
mucus
goblet cell (secreting mucus)
nucleus

CHEMICAL BARRIERS

1) The EYES

<u>Eyes</u> produce (in <u>tears</u>) a chemical called <u>lysozyme</u> which <u>kills bacteria</u> on the surface of the eye.

2) The STOMACH

If you eat <u>food</u> that contains pathogens, most of them will be <u>killed</u> by the <u>hydrochloric acid</u> in the <u>stomach</u>.

Coughs and sneezes spread diseases...

Lovely... anyway, after you've finished going eeuuurgh, make sure you remember the <u>six</u> different ways diseases can be spread and an <u>example</u> of a disease for each. Learn the <u>four barriers</u> too. And then wash your hands.

More About Drugs

I bet you've never <u>sat down</u> and had a <u>good think</u> about just how useful plants are to us. They produce all sorts of <u>chemicals</u> which are dead useful...

Plants Can Produce Chemicals to Defend Themselves

1) When <u>plants</u> are attacked by pathogens they can produce <u>chemicals</u> to defend themselves.

2) Some of these chemicals have <u>antibacterial</u> effects that protect the plant against <u>bacteria</u>.

3) Humans have been using these <u>plant chemicals</u> for centuries.

EXAMPLE: TEA TREE

- The <u>tea tree</u> is a large Australian shrub — its leaves produce an <u>oil</u> that <u>kills bacteria</u>.

- The indigenous people of Australia have used these leaves in their <u>traditional medicines</u> for centuries.

- These days the <u>purified oil</u> is used in all sorts of <u>antibacterial products</u>, e.g. <u>facial cleansers</u>.

Antiseptics Are Used Outside The Body To Stop Disease Spreading

1) <u>Antiseptics</u> are chemicals that <u>destroy bacteria</u> or <u>stop them growing</u>.

2) Antiseptics are used <u>outside</u> the body to help to <u>clean wounds</u> and <u>surfaces</u>. They're used to <u>prevent infection</u> rather than treat it.

3) Plenty of <u>household products</u> contain antiseptics, e.g. bathroom cleaners.

4) Antiseptics are used in <u>hospitals</u> and surgeries to try to prevent the spread of infections like MRSA (p.31).

Antibiotics Are Used Inside The Body To Treat Infections

1) Antibiotics are drugs used <u>inside</u> the body, usually taken as a pill or injected.

2) They are used to treat patients who are <u>already infected</u> with <u>bacteria</u> or <u>fungi</u>.

3) However, antibiotics don't destroy <u>viruses</u> (e.g. flu and cold viruses).

4) There are two types of <u>antibiotics</u>:

ANTIBACTERIALS

1) <u>Antibacterial antibiotics</u> (e.g. penicillin) are used to treat bacterial infections.

2) They work by <u>killing</u> bacteria or stopping them from <u>growing</u>.

3) However, bacteria can evolve <u>resistance</u> to certain antibacterial antibiotics — meaning the antibiotics <u>don't work any more</u> (see page 31).

ANTIFUNGALS

1) <u>Antifungal antibiotics</u> (e.g. nystatin) are used to treat fungal infections.

2) They work by <u>killing</u> the fungi or stopping them from <u>growing</u>.

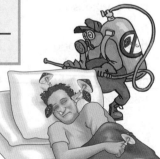

Imagine the hilarity when my Dad's sister married Mr Biotic...

So, we can take the <u>chemicals</u> that plants make to stop them being infected by <u>pathogens</u>, turn them into <u>useful products</u> and use them for our own benefits... How amazingly good is that? Even if you don't think so, just make sure you learn the page anyway, including the <u>differences</u> between <u>antiseptics</u>, <u>antibacterials</u> and <u>antifungals</u>.

Antiseptics and Antibiotics

The discovery of the first <u>antibiotic</u> was a huge one — suddenly infections that had been fatal could be <u>cured</u>.

Bacteria Can Become Resistant to Antibiotics

1) Bacteria can <u>mutate</u> — sometimes the mutations cause them to be <u>resistant</u> to (not killed by) an <u>antibiotic</u>.

2) If you have an <u>infection</u>, some of the bacteria might be <u>resistant</u> to antibiotics.

3) This means that when you <u>treat</u> the infection, only the <u>non-resistant</u> strains of bacteria will be <u>killed</u>.

4) The individual <u>resistant</u> bacteria will <u>survive</u> and <u>reproduce</u>, and the population of the resistant strain will <u>increase</u>. This is an example of natural selection (see page 13).

5) This resistant strain could cause a <u>serious infection</u> that <u>can't</u> be treated by antibiotics.
E.g. <u>MRSA</u> (methicillin-resistant *Staphylococcus aureus*) causes serious wound infections and is resistant to the powerful antibiotic <u>methicillin</u>.

6) <u>Misuse</u> of antibiotics (e.g. doctors <u>overprescribing</u> them or patients <u>not finishing a course</u>) has increased the <u>rate</u> of development of <u>resistant strains</u>. So nowadays you <u>won't</u> get antibiotics for a mild infection, only for something <u>more serious</u>.

You Can do a Practical to Investigate Antibiotics and Antiseptics

You can test the action of <u>antibiotics</u> by <u>growing</u> cultures of <u>microorganisms</u>:

1) Pour <u>hot</u>, sterilised agar jelly into a sterile <u>Petri dish</u> (a shallow round plastic dish).
(The jelly is a <u>culture medium</u> that contains the <u>carbohydrates</u>, <u>minerals</u>, <u>proteins</u> and <u>vitamins</u> that microorganisms need to grow.)

2) When the jelly's cooled and set, <u>transfer bacteria</u> to the culture medium.

3) Then take three paper discs — soak one disc in an <u>antibiotic</u> (disc A), another in a <u>different antibiotic</u> (disc B) and the third in <u>sterile water</u> (disc C).

4) Place the discs <u>onto the jelly</u> (labelling the bottom of the dish to show which disc is which) and tape the <u>lid</u> onto the dish.

5) Leave the dish for 24 hours at 25 °C. (The bacteria will <u>multiply</u> and grow into a 'lawn' covering the jelly.)

6) After that time look at the Petri dish for the results:

   • Anywhere the bacteria can't grow is called an "<u>inhibition zone</u>". The <u>bigger</u> the inhibition zone around a disc, the <u>more effective</u> the antibiotic is. E.g. in the diagram, antibiotic A is more effective than antibiotic B because it has a bigger inhibition zone.

   • There will be no inhibition zone around disc C because it's a <u>control</u> — it shows that it is the <u>antibiotic</u> and <u>not</u> the <u>paper disc</u> that is stopping the bacteria from growing.

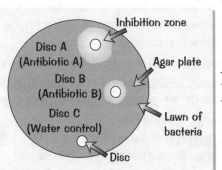

No inhibition zone around an antibiotic disc could mean that the bacteria are resistant to it (see top of page).

7) The control variables for this experiment include:

   • <u>Temperature</u> (e.g. don't leave one side of the dish near a radiator).

   • <u>Size</u> of the <u>discs</u>.

   • <u>Concentration</u> of the <u>antibiotics</u>.

8) Remember you can carry out exactly the same experiment as above using different <u>antiseptics</u>.

Agar — my favourite jelly flavour after raspberry...

Microorganisms might be the perfect <u>pets</u>. You don't have to walk them, they won't get lonely and they hardly cost anything to feed. But whatever you do, do <u>not</u> feed them after midnight.

Energy and Biomass

All living things are <u>interdependent</u> — organisms <u>depend on each other</u> for things like <u>food</u>, <u>pollination</u>, <u>shelter</u>, etc. in order to <u>survive</u> and <u>reproduce</u>. A simple example is that <u>bees</u> depend on <u>flowers</u> for <u>nectar</u> (food), and <u>flowers</u> depend on <u>bees</u> for <u>pollination</u>.

Some Energy Passes Along The Food Chain — But Most Is Lost

1) Energy from the <u>Sun</u> is the <u>source of energy</u> for nearly <u>all life on Earth</u>.

2) <u>Plants</u> convert <u>a small %</u> of the light energy that falls on them <u>into glucose</u>. The <u>rabbit</u> then <u>eats</u> the <u>plant</u>. It <u>uses up</u> some of the energy it gets from the plant — some of the rest is <u>stored</u> in its body. Then the <u>fox eats</u> the <u>rabbit</u> and gets some of the energy stored in the rabbit's body. This is a simple <u>food chain</u>.

3) Energy is used up at each stage to <u>stay alive</u>, i.e. in <u>respiration</u>, which powers <u>all life processes</u>, including <u>movement</u>. A lot of energy is <u>lost to the surroundings</u> as <u>heat</u>. This is especially true for <u>mammals and birds</u>, whose bodies must be kept at a <u>constant temperature</u> — normally higher than their surroundings.

4) This energy is said to be '<u>lost</u>' — it doesn't actually disappear but the next animal in the food chain can't use it.

5) <u>Material and energy</u> are also lost from the food chain in <u>droppings</u> — if you set dried droppings alight they burn, proving they still have chemical energy in them.

6) This explains why you hardly ever get <u>food chains</u> with more than about <u>five trophic levels</u>. So much energy is lost at each stage that there's not enough left to support more organisms after four or five stages.

Pyramids of Biomass Show Weight

1) <u>Biomass</u> is how much the creatures at each level of a food chain would <u>weigh</u> if you <u>put them together</u>.

2) This biomass is a <u>store</u> of <u>energy</u> (see above). So a pyramid of biomass also shows <u>how much energy</u> there is at <u>each stage</u> in the <u>food chain</u>.

3) The pyramid of biomass below shows the <u>food chain</u> of a mini meadow ecosystem. The dandelions are the <u>producer</u> (starting point) — they're eaten by the rabbits (primary consumers), which are eaten by the fox (secondary consumer)... and so on.

4) If you weighed them, all the <u>dandelions</u> would have a <u>big biomass</u> and the <u>hundreds of fleas</u> would have <u>a very small biomass</u>. Biomass pyramids are <u>always a pyramid shape</u>.

5) Each time you go <u>up</u> one level (one <u>trophic level</u> if you fancy showing off), the mass of organisms goes <u>down</u>. This is because most of the <u>biomass</u> (or <u>energy</u>) is lost (as shown above) and so <u>does not</u> become biomass in the <u>next level up</u>.

Don't forget that if you get a question on <u>biomass</u> in the exam you need to include the <u>units</u>. And if you're asked to <u>draw a pyramid</u>, make sure it's <u>to scale</u>.

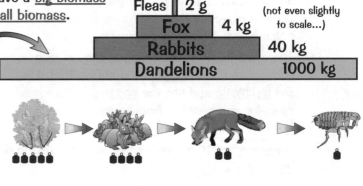

Fleas | 2 g
Fox | 4 kg
Rabbits | 40 kg
Dandelions | 1000 kg

(not even slightly to scale...)

Pyramids of Biomass — the eighth wonder of the world...

Pyramids of biomass are a way of describing food chains <u>quantitatively</u> (rather than just saying 'foxes eat rabbits', you say <u>what mass of foxes</u> eats <u>what mass of rabbits</u>, etc.). Don't forget that there's energy in that biomass and that energy is lost each time you go up a level in the pyramid e.g. in droppings, through movement.

Parasitism and Mutualism

For some species, their survival is almost completely <u>dependent</u> on another species. In a <u>parasitic</u> relationship, only <u>one</u> benefits — the other often suffers. But in a <u>mutualistic</u> relationship, <u>both</u> species benefit.

Parasites _Take Without Giving_ Anything In Return

<u>PARASITES</u> live in or on a host. They <u>take</u> what they need to survive, <u>without</u> giving anything <u>back</u>. This often <u>harms</u> the host — which makes it a win-lose situation. Here are some examples:

The host is the organism that a parasite lives on or in.

FLEAS

<u>Fleas</u> are insects that live in the fur and bedding of animals, including <u>humans</u>. They <u>feed</u> by <u>sucking the blood</u> of their hosts and can reproduce quickly. Their hosts <u>gain nothing</u> from having fleas (unless you count hundreds of bites).

HEAD LICE

<u>Head lice</u> are insects that live on <u>human scalps</u>, sucking <u>blood</u> for <u>food</u> and making the person <u>itch</u>.

TAPEWORMS

<u>Tapeworms</u> attach to the <u>intestinal wall</u> of their hosts (e.g. humans). They absorb lots of <u>nutrients</u> from the host, causing them to suffer from <u>malnutrition</u>.

MISTLETOE

<u>Mistletoe</u> is a <u>parasitic plant</u> that grows on <u>trees and shrubs</u>. It absorbs <u>water</u> and <u>nutrients</u> from its host, which can <u>reduce</u> the <u>host's growth</u>.

Both _Organisms Gain From a Mutualistic_ Relationship

<u>MUTUALISM</u> is a relationship where <u>both</u> organisms benefit — so it's a win-win relationship. For example:

OXPECKERS

<u>Oxpeckers</u> are birds that live on the backs of <u>buffalo</u>. Not only do they <u>eat pests</u> on the buffalo, like ticks, flies and maggots (providing the oxpeckers with a source of <u>food</u>), but they also <u>alert</u> the animal to any <u>predators</u> that are near, by hissing. Oxpeckers are an example of a <u>cleaner species</u>.

CLEANER FISH

Another example of cleaner species are <u>cleaner fish</u> (e.g. <u>cleaner wrasses</u>) that eat <u>dead skin</u> and <u>parasites</u> off <u>larger fish</u> (e.g. <u>groupers</u>). In return they get a source of <u>food</u>, and avoid being <u>eaten</u> by the big fish.

NITROGEN-FIXING BACTERIA IN LEGUMES

Most plants have to rely on <u>nitrogen-fixing bacteria</u> in the soil to get the <u>nitrates</u> that they need. But <u>leguminous plants</u> (beans, peas, clover etc.) carry the bacteria in <u>nodules</u> in their <u>roots</u>. The bacteria get a constant supply of <u>sugar</u> from the plant, and the plant gets essential <u>nitrates</u> from the bacteria.

CHEMOSYNTHETIC BACTERIA IN DEEP-SEA VENTS

Some <u>chemosynthetic bacteria</u> live inside <u>giant tube worms</u> or in the gills of <u>molluscs</u> in <u>deep-sea vents</u> (see page 12). The tube worms supply the bacteria with <u>chemicals</u> from the seawater, which the bacteria turn into <u>food</u> for themselves <u>and</u> the host worms.

Revision stress — don't let it eat you up...

Ugh... I can't believe there are animals out there that actually eat ticks and maggots. Makes me feel ill just thinking about it. That said, I do like the idea of something watching my back — that's kinda cool.

Human Activity and the Environment

Whichever way you look at it, human activity has an <u>enormous impact</u> on the environment...

A Larger Population Affects the Environment More

1) The <u>population</u> of the world is currently <u>rising pretty darn quickly</u> — as the graph shows.

2) This is mostly due to <u>modern medicine</u>, which has stopped widespread death from <u>disease</u>.

3) It's also due to modern farming methods, which can now provide the <u>food</u> needed for so many hungry mouths.

4) The effect of this is quite simple: MORE HUMANS = GREATER IMPACT.

5) There are potential problems...
   i)   raw materials, including <u>non-renewable</u> energy resources, are rapidly being <u>used up</u>,
   ii) more and more <u>waste</u> is being <u>produced</u>,
   iii) more and more <u>pollutants</u> are being <u>produced</u>, including <u>phosphates</u> (e.g. from detergents), <u>nitrates</u> (e.g. from fertilisers) and <u>sulfur dioxide</u> (e.g. from coal-burning power stations).

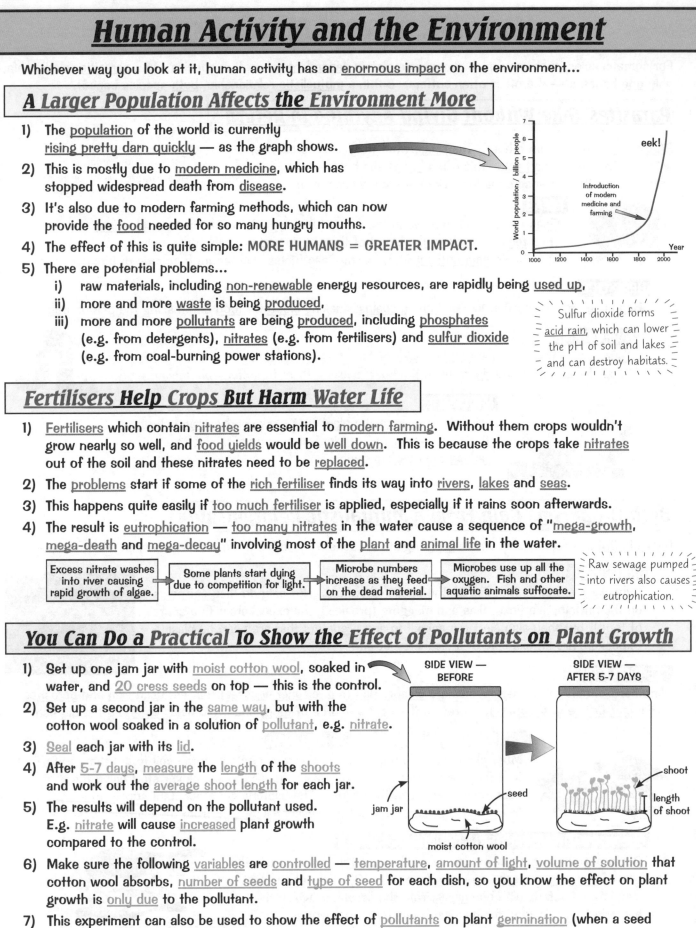

Sulfur dioxide forms <u>acid rain</u>, which can lower the pH of soil and lakes and can destroy habitats.

Fertilisers Help Crops But Harm Water Life

1) <u>Fertilisers</u> which contain <u>nitrates</u> are essential to <u>modern farming</u>. Without them crops wouldn't grow nearly so well, and <u>food yields</u> would be <u>well down</u>. This is because the crops take <u>nitrates</u> out of the soil and these nitrates need to be <u>replaced</u>.

2) The <u>problems</u> start if some of the <u>rich fertiliser</u> finds its way into <u>rivers</u>, <u>lakes</u> and <u>seas</u>.

3) This happens quite easily if <u>too much fertiliser</u> is applied, especially if it rains soon afterwards.

4) The result is <u>eutrophication</u> — <u>too many nitrates</u> in the water cause a sequence of "<u>mega-growth</u>, <u>mega-death</u> and <u>mega-decay</u>" involving most of the <u>plant</u> and <u>animal life</u> in the water.

| Excess nitrate washes into river causing rapid growth of algae. | → | Some plants start dying due to competition for light. | → | Microbe numbers increase as they feed on the dead material. | → | Microbes use up all the oxygen. Fish and other aquatic animals suffocate. |

Raw sewage pumped into rivers also causes eutrophication.

You Can Do a Practical To Show the Effect of Pollutants on Plant Growth

1) Set up one jam jar with <u>moist cotton wool</u>, soaked in water, and <u>20 cress seeds</u> on top — this is the control.

2) Set up a second jar in the <u>same way</u>, but with the cotton wool soaked in a solution of <u>pollutant</u>, e.g. <u>nitrate</u>.

3) <u>Seal</u> each jar with its <u>lid</u>.

4) After <u>5-7 days</u>, <u>measure</u> the <u>length</u> of the <u>shoots</u> and work out the <u>average shoot length</u> for each jar.

5) The results will depend on the pollutant used. E.g. <u>nitrate</u> will cause <u>increased</u> plant growth compared to the control.

6) Make sure the following <u>variables</u> are <u>controlled</u> — <u>temperature</u>, <u>amount of light</u>, <u>volume of solution</u> that cotton wool absorbs, <u>number of seeds</u> and <u>type of seed</u> for each dish, so you know the effect on plant growth is <u>only due</u> to the pollutant.

7) This experiment can also be used to show the effect of <u>pollutants</u> on plant <u>germination</u> (when a seed starts to grow into a plant).

SIDE VIEW — BEFORE

SIDE VIEW — AFTER 5-7 DAYS

jam jar

seed

moist cotton wool

shoot

length of shoot

Essential to plants, and essential to your biology revision...

<u>Nitrates</u> are essential to <u>plant growth</u> — so farmers add fertilisers to increase their crop yields. They could make your cress grow rampantly. But other pollutants like sulphur dioxide harm plants — expect fewer, smaller plants.

Recycling

Recycling is a good thing that humans can do to <u>reduce our impact</u> on the environment.
It means <u>reusing resources</u>, rather than using them once and chucking them in a waste dump.

Recycling Conserves Our Natural Resources

If materials aren't recycled they get <u>thrown away as waste</u>. This means that:

1) There is <u>more waste</u>, so <u>more land</u> has to be used for <u>landfill sites</u> (waste dumps).
Some waste is <u>toxic</u> (poisonous), so this also means more polluted land.

2) <u>More materials</u> have to be <u>manufactured</u> or <u>extracted</u> to make new products (rather than recycling existing ones) — using up more of the Earth's resources and more energy.

Recycling uses up less of the Earth's <u>natural resources</u>. <u>Recycling processes</u> usually use <u>less energy</u> and create <u>less pollution</u> than manufacturing or extracting materials from scratch. Recyclable materials include:

1) Metals Metals are <u>extracted</u> from <u>ores</u> (e.g. aluminium is extracted from bauxite).
There's a <u>limited amount</u> of metal ore — by recycling we make the most of what we've got.
Mining and extracting metals takes lots of <u>energy</u>, most of which comes from <u>burning fossil fuels</u>.
So recycling metals uses less of our <u>limited resources</u> of fossil fuels and means less CO_2 is released.

2) Paper Paper is produced from <u>wood</u>. <u>Recycling paper</u> means that <u>fewer trees</u> have to be <u>cut down</u>, which helps to <u>prevent deforestation</u>. <u>Recycling paper</u> uses <u>28%-70% less energy</u> than manufacturing new paper.

3) Plastics Most plastics are made from <u>crude oil</u> — so recycling plastics helps to <u>conserve</u> our <u>oil resources</u>. Plastics are really <u>slow to decompose</u> — if they're thrown away (rather than recycled), they take up space in landfill sites for years.

There are Some Problems with Recycling

1) Recycling still <u>uses energy</u>, e.g. for <u>collecting</u>, <u>sorting</u>, <u>cleaning</u> and <u>processing waste</u>.

2) Some waste materials can be difficult and <u>time-consuming to sort</u> out, e.g. different types of <u>plastic</u> have to be separated from each other before they can be recycled.

3) The <u>equipment needed</u> for recycling can be <u>expensive</u>, e.g. equipment for sorting plastics automatically.

4) In some cases, the <u>quality</u> of recycled materials <u>isn't as good</u> as new materials, e.g. recycled paper.

5) <u>Some materials</u> can only be <u>recycled</u> a <u>limited number of times</u> (e.g. plastics, paper). Others can be recycled indefinitely though (e.g. aluminium).

The UK Produces a Lot of Waste — and Could Recycle More

1) England and Wales produce over <u>100 million tonnes</u> of domestic, commercial and industrial <u>waste</u> a year.

2) The amount of waste <u>recycled</u> in the UK is <u>increasing</u> — but it's still not as much as some other European countries.

3) <u>New laws</u> are being introduced in the UK and the European Union (EU) to <u>increase recycling</u>, e.g. by 2015, EU law requires that cars will have to be made of 95% recyclable materials.

Recycling — doing the Tour de France twice...

Recycling isn't perfect — but it's generally a lot better than dumping all our rubbish in a big hole in the ground. Do your bit — <u>reuse plastic bags</u> and <u>recycle your drinks cans</u>.

Indicator Species

Some organisms <u>can't</u> live in areas where there is <u>polluted water</u> or <u>air</u>, but other organisms can. <u>Both</u> of these types of organism can be <u>monitored</u> and used as <u>indicators</u> of pollution — handy, as they're easy to spot, and show pollution levels over days and months.

Indicator Species *Are Used to Show The Level of...*

Some <u>organisms</u> are very <u>sensitive to changes</u> in their environment and so can be studied to see the effect of human activities — these organisms are known as <u>indicator species</u>.

① *Water Pollution*

1) If <u>raw sewage</u> or other pollutants containing <u>nitrates</u> are released into a <u>river</u>, the <u>bacterial population</u> in the water increases and uses up the <u>oxygen</u> (see page 34).

2) Some invertebrate animals, like <u>stonefly larvae</u> and <u>freshwater shrimps</u> are <u>good indicators</u> for water pollution because they're <u>very sensitive</u> to the concentration of <u>dissolved oxygen</u> in the water. If you find stonefly larvae in a river, it <u>indicates</u> that the <u>water is clean</u>.

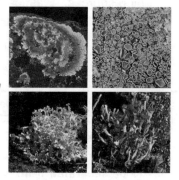

Stonefly larvae

Freshwater shrimps

3) Other <u>invertebrate</u> species have adapted to live in <u>polluted conditions</u> — so if you see a lot of them you know there's a problem. E.g. <u>blood worms</u> and <u>sludgeworms</u> indicate a <u>very high level of water pollution</u>.

② *Air Pollution*

1) <u>Air pollution</u> can be monitored by looking at particular types of <u>lichen</u> that are very sensitive to the concentration of <u>sulfur dioxide</u> in the atmosphere (and so can give a good idea about the level of pollution from <u>car exhausts</u>, power stations, etc.). The number and type of lichen at a particular location will indicate <u>how clean</u> the air is (e.g. the air is <u>clean</u> if there are <u>lots of lichen</u>).

2) <u>Blackspot fungus</u> is found on <u>rose leaves</u>. It is also sensitive to the level of sulfur dioxide in the air, so its presence will indicate <u>clean air</u>.

3) You might get some data on indicator species in the exam, e.g. data showing there are <u>more</u> lichen species <u>further away</u> from a city centre. This is probably because outside the city centre, there is <u>less pollution</u> and the air contains <u>less sulfur dioxide</u> and other pollutants.

Non-living Indicators *Can Also Show The Level of Pollution*

1) <u>Dissolved oxygen meters</u> and <u>chemical tests</u> are used to measure the concentration of dissolved oxygen in water, to show how the level of <u>water pollution</u> is changing.

2) <u>Electronic meters</u> and various <u>laboratory tests</u> are also used to measure the concentration of <u>sulfur dioxide</u> in air, to show how <u>air pollution</u> is changing.

Teenagers are an indicator species — not found in clean rooms...

Don't forget that the <u>absence</u> of an indicator species could mean the <u>opposite</u> of what they indicate. E.g. the <u>absence</u> of <u>stonefly larvae</u> could indicate <u>polluted water</u>. Nice and simple, innit?

The Carbon Cycle

Carbon flows through the Earth's ecosystems in the <u>carbon cycle</u>. The beauty of the carbon cycle is that carbon is <u>recycled</u> — it's <u>used by organisms</u> but then ends up back in the atmosphere again.

The Carbon Cycle Shows How Carbon *is Recycled*

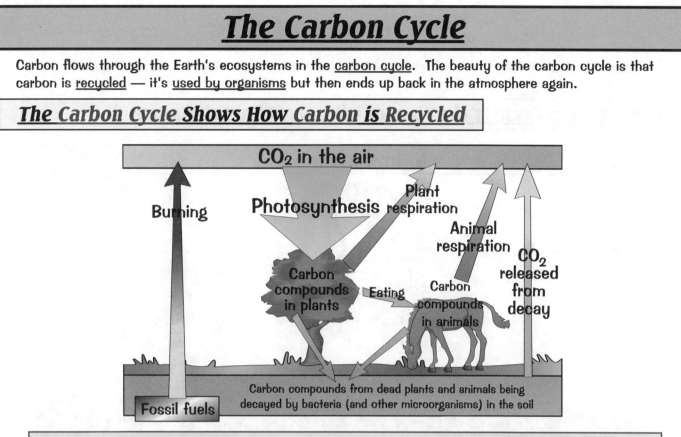

This diagram isn't half as bad as it looks. <u>Learn</u> these important points:

1) There's only <u>one arrow</u> going <u>down</u>. The only thing that <u>removes CO_2</u> from the atmosphere is <u>photosynthesis</u> — plants use it to make carbohydrates, fats and proteins.

2) <u>Eating</u> passes the carbon compounds in the plant along to <u>animals</u> in a food chain or web.

3) Both plant and animal <u>respiration</u> put CO_2 <u>back into the atmosphere</u>.

4) Plants and animals eventually <u>die</u> and <u>decay</u>.

5) When plants and animals <u>decay</u> they're broken down by <u>bacteria</u> and <u>fungi</u>.
These decomposers <u>release CO_2</u> back into the air by <u>respiration</u> as they break down the material.

6) <u>Fossil fuels</u> (made of decayed plant and animal matter) are <u>burned</u> (<u>combustion</u>).
This also <u>releases CO_2</u> back into the air.

Nutrients *are Constantly Recycled*

1) <u>Living things</u> are made of elements they take from the world around them.

2) It's not just carbon that plants take from the environment. <u>Plants</u> also take elements like <u>oxygen</u>, <u>hydrogen</u> and <u>nitrogen</u> (see the next page) from the <u>soil</u> or the <u>air</u>. They turn these elements into the <u>complex compounds</u> (carbohydrates, proteins and fats) that make up living organisms.

3) These elements are <u>returned</u> to the environment in <u>waste products</u> produced by the organisms, or when the organisms <u>die</u>. Dead organisms decay because they're <u>broken down</u> by <u>decomposers</u> — that's how the elements get put back into the <u>soil</u>.

4) All the important <u>elements</u> are <u>recycled</u> — they return to the soil or air, ready to be <u>used</u> by new <u>plants</u> and put back into the <u>food chain</u>.

What goes around, comes around...

In many ecosystems (like forests and prairies) the materials <u>taken out</u> of the soil and air are <u>balanced</u> by those that are put <u>back in</u>. There's a constant <u>cycle</u> happening. Changing ecosystems (e.g. bogs accumulating peat, plantations where trees are removed) don't exactly balance though. The <u>cycle</u> still happens, it's just a bit <u>wonky</u>.

The Nitrogen Cycle

The flow of nitrates through the atmosphere, soil and living organisms is called the nitrogen cycle. It's similar to the carbon cycle (last page) — but a tad more complicated...

The Nitrogen Cycle is the Flow of Nitrogen Through Nature

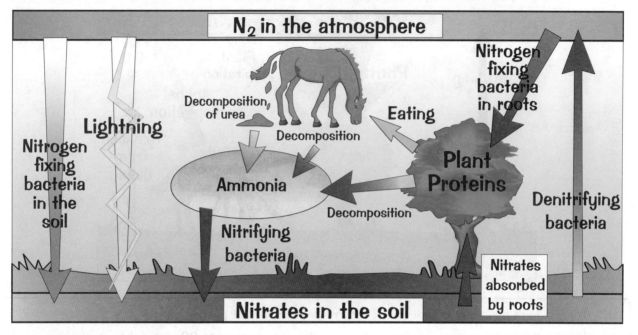

1) The atmosphere contains 78% nitrogen gas, N_2. This is very unreactive and so it can't be used directly by plants or animals.

2) Nitrogen is needed for making proteins for growth, so living organisms have to get it somehow.

3) Nitrogen in the air has to be turned into nitrogen compounds, e.g. nitrates, before plants can use it. Plants absorb nitrates from the soil and use them to make proteins. Animals can only get proteins by eating plants (or each other) — so nitrogen compounds are passed along a food chain.

4) Decomposers (e.g. bacteria, fungi, worms) in the soil break down dead plants and animals. Decomposer bacteria turn proteins (from dead plants and animals) and urea (in animal waste) into ammonia.

5) Other soil bacteria called nitrifying bacteria convert this ammonia into nitrates. Since nitrates can be taken up by plants, the nitrogen in these organisms is recycled.

6) Nitrogen fixation isn't an obsession with nitrogen — it's the process of turning N_2 from the air into nitrogen compounds in the soil which plants can use. There are two main ways that this happens:
   a) Lightning — there's so much energy in a bolt of lightning that it's enough to make nitrogen react with oxygen in the air to give nitrates.
   b) Nitrogen-fixing bacteria in roots and soil (see below).

7) There are four different types of bacteria involved in the nitrogen cycle:

   a) DECOMPOSER BACTERIA — decompose proteins and urea and turn them into ammonia.
   b) NITRIFYING BACTERIA — turn ammonia in decaying matter into nitrates.
   c) NITROGEN-FIXING BACTERIA — turn atmospheric N_2 into nitrogen compounds that plants can use.
   d) DENITRIFYING BACTERIA — turn nitrates back into N_2 gas. This is of no benefit to living organisms.

8) Some nitrogen-fixing bacteria live in the soil. Others live in nodules on the roots of legume plants (e.g. peas and beans). This is why legume plants are so good at putting nitrogen back into the soil. The plants have a mutualistic relationship with the bacteria (see page 33).

I wish I had some information-fixing bacteria...

The nitrogen cycle is probably the scariest looking diagram you'll see in the whole of GCSE Science. But learn it you must. The horse being in the sky is just a bit of artistic licence...

Revision Summary for B1 Topic 3

It's that time again — time to see whether any of the stuff you've been reading has managed to soak through the fluff, mothballs and mouldy pizza boxes into your spongy old brain. Here we go...

1) How does a stimulant drug work? Give two examples of stimulants.
2) Briefly describe an experiment you could use to measure reaction times.
3) Briefly describe the harmful effects of the following chemicals found in cigarette smoke:
   a) nicotine   b) tar   c) carbon monoxide
4) State two long-term effects of drinking too much alcohol.
5) Are there enough organs to supply everyone who needs a donor organ?
6) What is a pathogen?
7) What is a vector?
8) State four different ways that pathogens can be spread, and give an example of each.
9) Name one chemical and one physical barrier that form part of the defence against pathogens.
10) What do plants produce to defend themselves from bacteria?
11) What are antiseptics?
12) Name the two types of antibiotics.
13) Name one type of bacteria that has developed resistance to certain antibiotics.
14) Why shouldn't your doctor give you antibiotics for a mild infection?
15) Where does the energy in a food chain originate? What happens to the energy?
16) Not all energy and biomass passes from one trophic level to the next. Where does the rest go?
17) Why are pyramids of biomass always pyramid shaped?
18) What is the difference between a parasitic and a mutualistic relationship?
19) Give an example of:
   a) a parasitic relationship   b) a mutualistic relationship
20) Give three ways in which an increasing human population has a greater effect on the environment.
21) Explain what eutrophication is.
22) Give two advantages and two disadvantages of recycling.
23) Give three types of material which can be recycled.
24) What does it mean if you find stonefly larvae in a river?
   a) There are no stones in the river.   b) The water is clean.   c) The water is dirty.
25) Explain how lichen can be used as an indicator of air pollution.
26) Sketch the carbon cycle.
27) Give two ways in which the elements an animal eats can be returned to the environment.
28) Why is nitrogen needed by plants and animals?
29) What do decomposers do?
30) Sketch out the nitrogen cycle.

Cells and Microscopy

All living things are made of <u>cells</u>. When someone first peered down a microscope at a slice of cork and drew the <u>boxes</u> they saw, little did they know that they'd seen the <u>building blocks</u> of <u>every organism on the planet</u>.

Plant and Animal Cells have Similarities and Differences

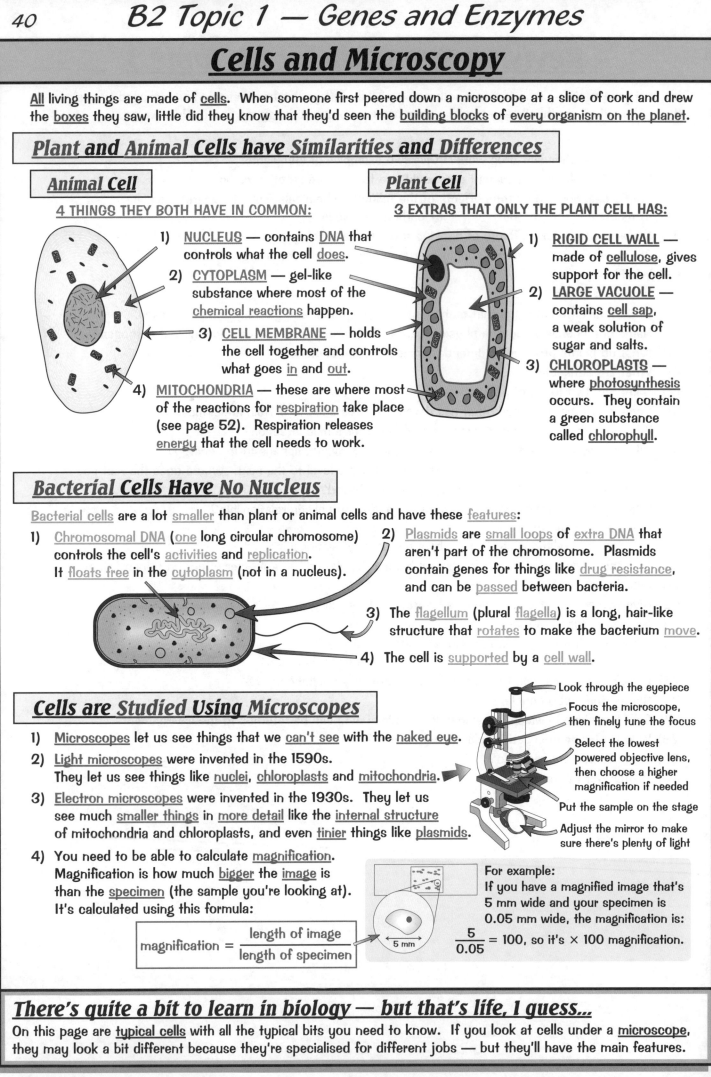

Animal Cell

4 THINGS THEY BOTH HAVE IN COMMON:

1) <u>NUCLEUS</u> — contains <u>DNA</u> that controls what the cell <u>does</u>.

2) <u>CYTOPLASM</u> — gel-like substance where most of the <u>chemical reactions</u> happen.

3) <u>CELL MEMBRANE</u> — holds the cell together and controls what goes <u>in</u> and <u>out</u>.

4) <u>MITOCHONDRIA</u> — these are where most of the reactions for <u>respiration</u> take place (see page 52). Respiration releases <u>energy</u> that the cell needs to work.

Plant Cell

3 EXTRAS THAT ONLY THE PLANT CELL HAS:

1) <u>RIGID CELL WALL</u> — made of <u>cellulose</u>, gives support for the cell.

2) <u>LARGE VACUOLE</u> — contains <u>cell sap</u>, a weak solution of sugar and salts.

3) <u>CHLOROPLASTS</u> — where <u>photosynthesis</u> occurs. They contain a green substance called <u>chlorophyll</u>.

Bacterial Cells Have No Nucleus

<u>Bacterial cells</u> are a lot <u>smaller</u> than plant or animal cells and have these <u>features</u>:

1) <u>Chromosomal DNA</u> (<u>one</u> long circular chromosome) controls the cell's <u>activities</u> and <u>replication</u>. It <u>floats free</u> in the <u>cytoplasm</u> (not in a nucleus).

2) <u>Plasmids</u> are <u>small loops</u> of <u>extra DNA</u> that aren't part of the chromosome. Plasmids contain genes for things like <u>drug resistance</u>, and can be <u>passed</u> between bacteria.

3) The <u>flagellum</u> (plural <u>flagella</u>) is a long, hair-like structure that <u>rotates</u> to make the bacterium <u>move</u>.

4) The cell is <u>supported</u> by a <u>cell wall</u>.

Cells are Studied Using Microscopes

1) <u>Microscopes</u> let us see things that we <u>can't see</u> with the <u>naked eye</u>.

2) <u>Light microscopes</u> were invented in the 1590s. They let us see things like <u>nuclei</u>, <u>chloroplasts</u> and <u>mitochondria</u>.

3) <u>Electron microscopes</u> were invented in the 1930s. They let us see much <u>smaller things</u> in <u>more detail</u> like the <u>internal structure</u> of mitochondria and chloroplasts, and even <u>tinier</u> things like <u>plasmids</u>.

4) You need to be able to calculate <u>magnification</u>. Magnification is how much <u>bigger</u> the <u>image</u> is than the <u>specimen</u> (the sample you're looking at). It's calculated using this formula:

Look through the eyepiece

Focus the microscope, then finely tune the focus

Select the lowest powered objective lens, then choose a higher magnification if needed

Put the sample on the stage

Adjust the mirror to make sure there's plenty of light

$$\text{magnification} = \frac{\text{length of image}}{\text{length of specimen}}$$

For example:
If you have a magnified image that's 5 mm wide and your specimen is 0.05 mm wide, the magnification is:

$\frac{5}{0.05} = 100$, so it's × 100 magnification.

5 mm

There's quite a bit to learn in biology — but that's life, I guess...

On this page are <u>typical cells</u> with all the typical bits you need to know. If you look at cells under a <u>microscope</u>, they may look a bit different because they're specialised for different jobs — but they'll have the main features.

DNA

Once people had found out that <u>DNA</u> was the <u>molecule</u> that carried the <u>instructions</u> for <u>characteristics</u> from <u>your parents</u> to <u>you</u>, scientists did loads of studies to try and work out its <u>structure</u>. Here are their results...

DNA — a Double Helix of Paired Bases

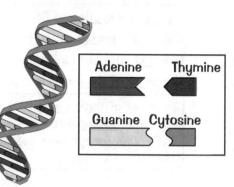

1) A DNA molecule has <u>two strands</u> coiled together in the shape of a <u>double helix</u> (two spirals), as shown in the diagram opposite.

2) The two strands are held together by chemicals called <u>bases</u>. There are <u>four</u> different bases (shown in the diagram as different colours) — <u>adenine</u> (A), <u>cytosine</u> (C), <u>guanine</u> (G) and <u>thymine</u> (T).

3) The bases are <u>paired</u>, and they always pair up in the same way — it's always <u>A-T</u> and <u>C-G</u>. This is called <u>base-pairing</u>.

4) The <u>base pairs</u> are joined together by <u>weak hydrogen bonds</u>.

5) A <u>gene</u> is a <u>section</u> of DNA, and the <u>sequence of bases</u> in a gene <u>code</u> for a <u>specific protein</u> — see page 42 for more.

Watson, Crick, Franklin and Wilkins Discovered The Structure of DNA

1) <u>Rosalind Franklin</u> and <u>Maurice Wilkins</u> worked out that DNA had a <u>helical structure</u> by directing beams of <u>x-rays</u> onto <u>crystallised DNA</u> and looking at the <u>patterns</u> the x-rays formed as they bounced off.

2) <u>James Watson</u> and <u>Francis Crick</u> used these ideas, along with the knowledge that the amount of <u>adenine + guanine</u> matched the amount of <u>thymine + cytosine</u>, to make a <u>model</u> of the DNA molecule where all the pieces <u>fitted together</u>.

You Can Do a Practical To Extract DNA From Cells

1) Chop up some <u>onion</u> and put it in a beaker containing a solution of <u>detergent</u> and <u>salt</u>. The detergent will <u>break down</u> the <u>cell membranes</u> and the salt will make the <u>DNA stick together</u>.

2) Put the beaker into a water bath at <u>60 °C</u> for <u>15 minutes</u> — this <u>denatures enzymes</u> (see p.44) that could digest the DNA and helps <u>soften</u> the onion cells.

3) Put the beaker in <u>ice</u> to <u>cool</u> the mixture down — this <u>stops</u> the DNA from <u>breaking down</u>.

4) Once the mixture is ice-cold, put it into a <u>blender</u> for a <u>few seconds</u> to <u>break open</u> the cell walls and <u>release</u> (but not break up) the DNA.

5) <u>Cool</u> the mixture down again, then <u>filter it</u> to get the froth and big bits of cell out.

6) <u>Gently</u> add some <u>ice-cold alcohol</u> to the filtered mixture. The <u>DNA</u> will start to <u>come out</u> of solution as it's <u>not soluble</u> in cold alcohol. It will appear as a <u>stringy white substance</u> that can be carefully fished out with a <u>glass rod</u>.

My band has a great rhythm section — it has paired basses...

Hope you enjoyed <u>extracting</u> all that DNA and learning about its <u>structure</u>. Sadly, though, you won't be getting a <u>Nobel prize</u> for your efforts — you're too late. Crick, Watson and Wilkins were awarded the Nobel prize for their work in <u>1962</u>. Unfortunately, by then Franklin had died and couldn't be nominated for the prize.

Protein Synthesis

Your DNA is basically a long list of instructions on how to make all the proteins in your body.

A Gene Codes for a Specific Protein

1) A gene is a section of DNA. It contains the instructions to make a specific protein.
2) Cells make proteins by stringing amino acids together in a particular order.
3) Only 20 different amino acids are used to make up thousands of different proteins.
4) The order of the bases in a gene simply tells cells in what order to put the amino acids together:

> Each set of three bases (called a triplet) codes for a particular amino acid.
> Here's an example (don't worry — you don't have to remember the specific codes):
> TAT codes for tyrosine and GCA for alanine. If the order of the bases in the gene is
> TAT-GCA-TAT then the order of amino acids in the protein will be tyrosine-alanine-tyrosine.

5) DNA also determines which genes are switched on or off — and so which proteins the cell produces, e.g. haemoglobin or keratin. That in turn determines what type of cell it is, e.g. red blood cell, skin cell.
6) Some of the proteins help to make all the other things that aren't made of protein (like cell membranes) from substances that come from your diet (like fats and minerals).

Proteins are Made by Ribosomes

Proteins are made in the cell by organelles called ribosomes. DNA is found in the cell nucleus and can't move out of it because it's really big. The cell needs to get the information from the DNA to the ribosome in the cell cytoplasm. This is done using a molecule called mRNA, which is very similar to DNA, but it's shorter and only a single strand. mRNA is like a messenger between the DNA in the nucleus and the ribosome.
Here's how it's done:

1) The two DNA strands unzip. The DNA is used as a template to make the mRNA. Base pairing ensures it's complementary (an exact match to the opposite strand). This step is called TRANSCRIPTION.
2) The mRNA molecule moves out of the nucleus and joins with a ribosome.
3) Amino acids that match the mRNA code are brought to the ribosome by molecules called tRNA.
4) The job of the ribosome is to stick amino acids together in a chain to make a polypeptide (protein). This follows the order of the triplet of bases (called codons) in the mRNA. This step is called TRANSLATION.

mRNA molecule forming

mRNA

ribosome

protein   amino acids

The result of all this molecular jiggery-pokery is that each type of protein gets made with its own specific number and sequence of amino acids — the ones described by its DNA base sequence. This is what makes it fold up into the right shape to do its specific job, e.g. as a particular enzyme (see the next page).

Mutations can be Harmful, Beneficial or Neutral

A mutation is a change to an organism's DNA base sequence. This could affect the sequence of amino acids in the protein, which could affect the shape of the protein and so its function. In turn, this could affect the characteristics of an organism. Mutations can be harmful, beneficial or neutral:

HARMFUL A mutation could cause a genetic disorder, for example cystic fibrosis.

BENEFICIAL A mutation could produce a new characteristic that is beneficial to an organism, e.g. a mutation in genes on bacterial plasmids can make them resistant to antibiotics.

NEUTRAL Some mutations are neither harmful nor beneficial, e.g. they don't affect a protein's function.

4 bases, 20 amino acids, 1000s of proteins...

The order of bases says what amino acid is added and the order of amino acids determines the type of protein.

B2 Topic 1 — Genes and Enzymes

Enzymes

Chemical reactions are what make you work. And enzymes are what make them work.

Enzymes Are Catalysts Produced by Living Things

1) Living things have thousands of different chemical reactions going on inside them all the time.

2) These reactions need to be carefully controlled — to get the right amounts of substances.

3) You can usually make a reaction happen more quickly by raising the temperature.
   This would speed up the useful reactions but also the unwanted ones too... not good.

4) So... living things produce enzymes which act as biological catalysts. Enzymes reduce the need for high temperatures and we only have enzymes to speed up the useful chemical reactions in the body.

> A **CATALYST** is a substance which **INCREASES** the speed of a reaction,
> without being **CHANGED** or **USED UP** in the reaction.

5) Enzymes are all proteins, and they all work in the same way to catalyse various reactions.
   They can work inside or outside cells, for example:

   • DNA replication — enzymes help copy a cell's DNA before it divides by mitosis or meiosis (see p.47-48).

   • Protein synthesis — enzymes hold amino acids in place and form bonds between them (see p.42).

   • Digestion — various enzymes are secreted into the gut to digest different food molecules (see p.66).

Enzymes Have Special Shapes So They Can Catalyse Reactions

1) Chemical reactions usually involve things either being split apart or joined together.

2) The substrate is the molecule changed in the reaction.

3) Every enzyme has an active site — the part where it joins on to its substrate to catalyse the reaction.

4) Enzymes are really picky — they usually only work with one substrate. The posh way of saying this is that enzymes have a high specificity for their substrate.

5) This is because, for the enzyme to work, the substrate has to fit into the active site. If the substrate's shape doesn't match the active site's shape, then the reaction won't be catalysed. This is called the 'lock and key' mechanism, because the substrate fits into the enzyme just like a key fits into a lock.

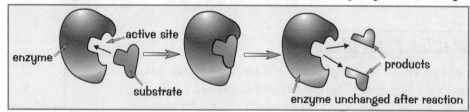

Measuring the Rate of an Enzyme-Controlled Reaction — Method

1) You can measure the rate of a reaction by using amylase as the enzyme and starch as the substrate.

2) Amylase catalyses the breakdown of starch, so you can time how long it takes for the starch to disappear.

3) To do this, regularly take a drop of the amylase and starch mixture, and put it onto a drop of iodine solution on a spotting tile. Record the colour change — it'll turn blue-black if starch is present. Note the time when the iodine solution no longer turns blue-black — the starch has then been broken down by the amylase.

4) You can use the times to compare reaction rates under different conditions — see the next page.

If the lock & key mechanism fails, you get in through a window...

Just like you've got to have the correct key for a lock, you've got to have the right substrate for an enzyme.

More on Enzymes

Now it's time to take the method you've just learnt for an enzyme-controlled reaction and put it into practice...

Measuring the Rate of an Enzyme-Controlled Reaction — Variables

In the amylase/starch experiment from the last page you need to choose which variable to change.
For example:

- to investigate the effect of temperature, put the test tubes into water baths at a range of temperatures
- to investigate the effect of pH, use a range of different pH buffers
- to investigate the effect of substrate concentration, vary the initial concentrations of the starch solutions.

Remember to keep all the variables you're not investigating constant, e.g. use the same amylase concentration each time.

Measuring the Rate of an Enzyme-Controlled Reaction — Results

Enzymes Like it Warm but Not Too Hot

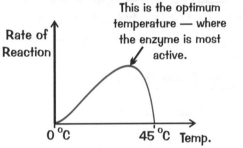

This is the optimum temperature — where the enzyme is most active.

1) Changing the temperature changes the rate of an enzyme-catalysed reaction.

2) Like with any reaction, a higher temperature increases the rate at first. This is because more heat means the enzymes and the substrate particles have more energy. They move about more, so they're more likely to meet up and react.

3) If it gets too hot though, some of the bonds holding the enzyme together break.

4) This makes the enzyme lose its shape. Its active site doesn't fit the shape of the substrate any more, so it can't catalyse the reaction and the reaction stops.

5) The enzyme is denatured — it won't go back to its normal shape if things cool down again.

6) Each enzyme has its own optimum temperature when the reaction goes fastest. This is the temperature just before it gets too hot and starts to denature. The optimum temperature for the most important human enzymes is about 37 °C — the same temperature as our bodies. Lucky for us.

Enzymes Like it the Right pH Too

1) The pH also has an effect on enzymes. If it's too high or too low, it interferes with the bonds holding the enzyme together. This changes the shape of the active site and denatures the enzyme.

2) All enzymes have an optimum pH that they work best at. It's often neutral pH 7, but not always. For example, pepsin is an enzyme used to break down proteins in the stomach. It works best at pH 2, which means it's well-suited to the acidic conditions in the stomach.

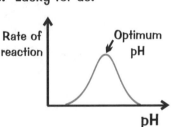

Substrate Concentration Affects the Rate of Reaction Up to a Point

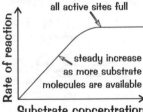

all active sites full

steady increase as more substrate molecules are available

1) The higher the substrate concentration, the faster the reaction — it's more likely the enzyme will meet up and react with a substrate molecule.

2) This is only true up to a point though. After that, there are so many substrate molecules that the enzymes have about as much as they can cope with (all the active sites are full), and adding more makes no difference.

If only enzymes could speed up revision...

Changing the shape of a protein totally changes it. Egg white contains lots of protein — think what happens when you boil an egg and denature the protein. It goes from clear and runny to white and solid.

The Human Genome Project

The Human Genome Project is one of the most exciting things to happen in science for ages. Some people have even called it "more exciting than the first moon landing". Alright, maybe they should get out more...

The Idea was to Map the 25 000 (or so) Human Genes

Thousands of scientists from all over the world collaborated (worked together) on the Human Genome Project. The big idea was to find every single human gene. Human DNA is made up of about 25 000 genes curled up to form 23 chromosomes (the other 23 will have the same genes — but maybe different versions).

If scientists work together, they can share resources and cut down costs.

The collaboration of lots of scientists meant that all the genes were found more quickly and the data could be made public. Now we've found all the genes, the next thing is to try to figure out what they all do...

> If you get an exam question on this stuff, they'll probably ask you what's good about it, what's bad about it, or what's good and bad about it.

The Good Stuff — Improving Medicine and Forensic Science

1) **PREDICT AND PREVENT DISEASES**
   If doctors knew what genes predisposed people to what diseases, we could all get individually tailored advice on the best diet and lifestyle to avoid our likely problems. And doctors could check us regularly to ensure early treatment if we do develop the diseases we're susceptible to. Better still, cures could be found for genetic diseases like cystic fibrosis and sickle cell anaemia.

2) **DEVELOP NEW AND BETTER MEDICINES**
   Maybe one day we'll all have medicines designed especially for us — these will be based on the way our individual body will react to the disease and to the possible treatments. More generally, knowing how a disease affects us on a molecular level makes it possible to design more effective treatments.

3) **ACCURATE DIAGNOSES**
   Some diseases are hard to test for (e.g. you can only tell for sure if someone has Alzheimer's after they die), but if we know the genetic cause, accurate testing will be a lot easier.

4) **IMPROVE FORENSIC SCIENCE**
   Forensic scientists can produce a 'DNA fingerprint' from biological material found at a crime scene. If this matches your suspect's DNA... he or she was almost certainly present.

   In the future, it might even be possible to figure out what a suspect looks like from DNA found at the scene of a crime (e.g. their eye, hair and skin colour).

The Bad Stuff — It Could be a Scary World If You're not Perfect

1) **INCREASED STRESS**
   If someone knew from an early age that they're susceptible to a nasty brain disease, they could panic every time they get a headache (even if they never get the disease).

2) **GENE-ISM**
   People with genetic problems could come under pressure not to have children.

3) **DISCRIMINATION BY EMPLOYERS AND INSURERS**
   Life insurance could become impossible to get (or blummin' expensive at least) if you have any genetic likelihood of serious disease. And employers may discriminate against people who are genetically likely to get a disease.

DNA lipstick is part of my genetic make-up...

Remember that these are only possibilities — some may happen soon, some will take ages, and others might not happen at all. But it's exciting stuff (medicines just for you — gosh). But before you can come to a sensible decision about the ethics of it all, you must know the facts. No problem — you were going to learn it all anyway.

Genetic Engineering

Scientists can now <u>change</u> an organism's <u>genes</u> to alter its characteristics.
This is a new science with exciting possibilities, but there might be <u>dangers</u> too...

Genetic Engineering <u>Uses</u> Enzymes <u>to Cut and Paste</u> Genes

The basic idea is to move <u>useful genes</u> from one organisms's chromosomes into the cells of another...

1) A useful gene is "<u>cut</u>" out from one organism's chromosome using <u>enzymes</u>.

2) <u>Enzymes</u> are then used to <u>cut</u> another organism's chromosome and then to <u>insert</u> the useful gene.

3) This technique produces <u>genetically modified</u> (<u>GM</u>) organisms.
   E.g. <u>human genes</u> can be used to make <u>GM bacteria</u>:

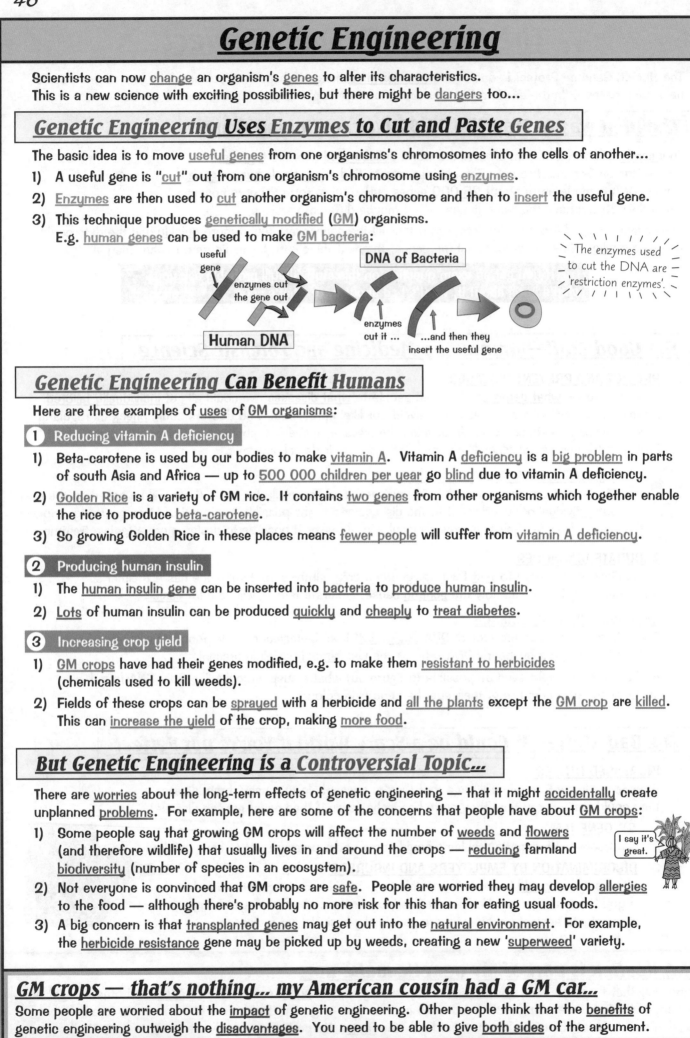

useful gene

enzymes cut the gene out

Human DNA

DNA of Bacteria

enzymes cut it ...

...and then they insert the useful gene

The enzymes used to cut the DNA are 'restriction enzymes'.

Genetic Engineering <u>Can Benefit</u> Humans

Here are three examples of <u>uses</u> of <u>GM organisms</u>:

1 Reducing vitamin A deficiency

1) Beta-carotene is used by our bodies to make <u>vitamin A</u>. Vitamin A <u>deficiency</u> is a <u>big problem</u> in parts of south Asia and Africa — up to <u>500 000 children per year</u> go <u>blind</u> due to vitamin A deficiency.

2) <u>Golden Rice</u> is a variety of GM rice. It contains <u>two genes</u> from other organisms which together enable the rice to produce <u>beta-carotene</u>.

3) So growing Golden Rice in these places means <u>fewer people</u> will suffer from <u>vitamin A deficiency</u>.

2 Producing human insulin

1) The <u>human insulin gene</u> can be inserted into <u>bacteria</u> to <u>produce human insulin</u>.

2) <u>Lots</u> of human insulin can be produced <u>quickly</u> and <u>cheaply</u> to <u>treat diabetes</u>.

3 Increasing crop yield

1) <u>GM crops</u> have had their genes modified, e.g. to make them <u>resistant to herbicides</u> (chemicals used to kill weeds).

2) Fields of these crops can be <u>sprayed</u> with a herbicide and <u>all the plants</u> except the <u>GM crop</u> are <u>killed</u>. This can <u>increase the yield</u> of the crop, making <u>more food</u>.

But Genetic Engineering is a <u>Controversial Topic...</u>

There are <u>worries</u> about the long-term effects of genetic engineering — that it might <u>accidentally</u> create unplanned <u>problems</u>. For example, here are some of the concerns that people have about <u>GM crops</u>:

1) Some people say that growing GM crops will affect the number of <u>weeds</u> and <u>flowers</u> (and therefore wildlife) that usually lives in and around the crops — <u>reducing</u> farmland <u>biodiversity</u> (number of species in an ecosystem).

I say it's great.

2) Not everyone is convinced that GM crops are <u>safe</u>. People are worried they may develop <u>allergies</u> to the food — although there's probably no more risk for this than for eating usual foods.

3) A big concern is that <u>transplanted genes</u> may get out into the <u>natural environment</u>. For example, the <u>herbicide resistance</u> gene may be picked up by weeds, creating a new '<u>superweed</u>' variety.

GM crops — that's nothing... my American cousin had a GM car...

Some people are worried about the <u>impact</u> of genetic engineering. Other people think that the <u>benefits</u> of genetic engineering outweigh the <u>disadvantages</u>. You need to be able to give <u>both sides</u> of the argument.

Mitosis

The cells of your body <u>divide</u> to <u>produce more cells</u>. This is so that your body can <u>grow</u> and <u>repair</u> damaged tissues. Of course, cell division doesn't just happen in humans — animals and plants do it too.

Mitosis Makes New Cells for Growth and Repair

1) <u>Human body cells</u> are <u>diploid</u>. This means they have <u>two versions</u> of each <u>chromosome</u> — one from the person's <u>mother</u>, and one from their <u>father</u>. This diagram shows the <u>23 pairs of chromosomes</u> in a human cell.

2) When a cell <u>divides</u> it makes <u>two</u> cells <u>identical</u> to the <u>original</u> cell — each with a <u>nucleus</u> containing the <u>same number</u> of chromosomes as the original cell.

3) This type of cell division is called <u>mitosis</u>. It's used when humans (and animals and plants) want to <u>grow</u> or to <u>replace</u> cells that have been <u>damaged</u>.

Mitosis Results in Two Identical Cells

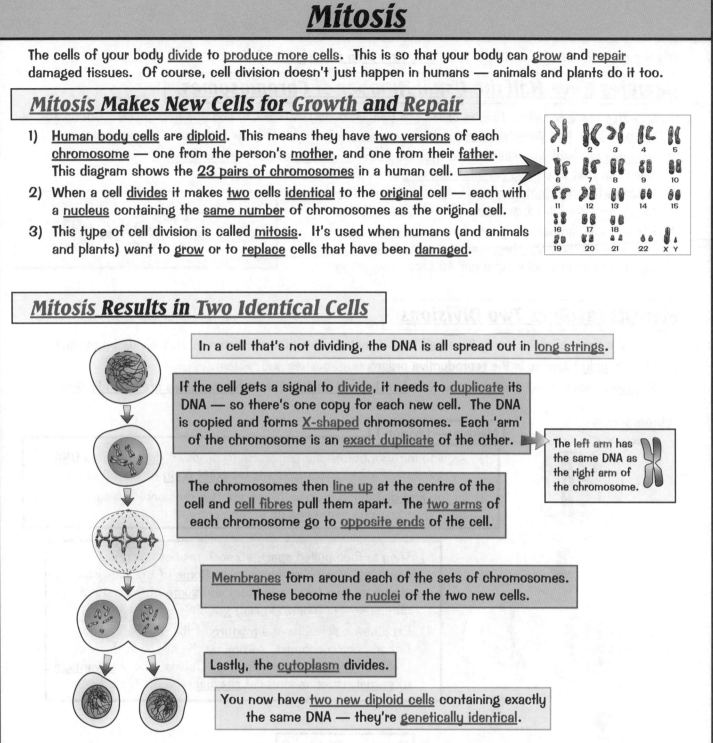

In a cell that's not dividing, the DNA is all spread out in <u>long strings</u>.

If the cell gets a signal to <u>divide</u>, it needs to <u>duplicate</u> its DNA — so there's one copy for each new cell. The DNA is copied and forms <u>X-shaped</u> chromosomes. Each 'arm' of the chromosome is an <u>exact duplicate</u> of the other.

The left arm has the same DNA as the right arm of the chromosome.

The chromosomes then <u>line up</u> at the centre of the cell and <u>cell fibres</u> pull them apart. The <u>two arms</u> of each chromosome go to <u>opposite ends</u> of the cell.

<u>Membranes</u> form around each of the sets of chromosomes. These become the <u>nuclei</u> of the two new cells.

Lastly, the <u>cytoplasm</u> divides.

You now have <u>two new diploid cells</u> containing exactly the same DNA — they're <u>genetically identical</u>.

Asexual Reproduction Also Uses Mitosis

1) Some organisms also <u>reproduce</u> by mitosis, e.g. strawberry plants form runners in this way, which become new plants.

2) This is an example of <u>asexual reproduction</u>.

3) The offspring have exactly the <u>same genes</u> as the parent — so there's <u>no genetic variation</u>.

Now that I have your undivided attention...

The next page is about meiosis, which is quite similar to mitosis. It's easy to get them confused if you're not careful. So make sure you've <u>learnt mitosis really thoroughly</u>, before moving on. The best way to do this is to: 1) learn the diagram on this page, 2) cover it over, 3) sketch it out.

Meiosis

You thought mitosis was exciting. Hah. <u>You ain't seen nothing yet</u>.

Gametes Have Half the Usual Number of Chromosomes

1) <u>Gametes</u> are 'sex cells'. They're called <u>ova</u> (single, ovum) in females, and <u>sperm</u> in males. During <u>sexual reproduction</u>, two <u>gametes combine</u> to form a <u>new cell</u> which will grow to become a new organism.

2) <u>Gametes</u> are <u>haploid</u> — this means they only have <u>one copy</u> of each <u>chromosome</u>. This is so that when <u>two gametes combine</u> at fertilisation, the resulting cell (zygote) has the <u>right number of chromosomes</u>. Zygotes are <u>diploid</u> — they have <u>two copies</u> of each <u>chromosome</u>.

3) For example, human body cells have <u>46 chromosomes</u>. The <u>gametes</u> have <u>23 chromosomes each</u>, so that when an egg and sperm combine, you get 46 chromosomes again.

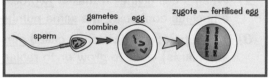

Meiosis Involves Two Divisions

1) To make new cells which only have <u>half</u> the original number of chromosomes, cells divide by <u>meiosis</u>.

2) Meiosis <u>only</u> happens in the <u>reproductive organs</u> (e.g. ovaries and testes).

3) <u>Meiosis</u> is when a cell divides to produce <u>four haploid nuclei</u> whose <u>chromosomes are NOT identical</u>.

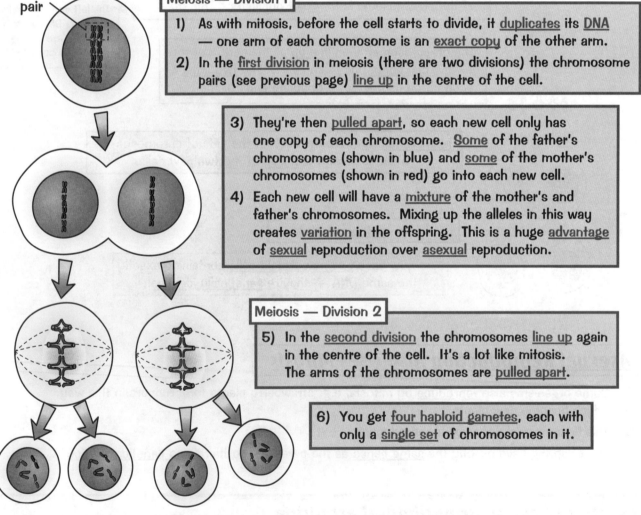

chromosome pair

Meiosis — Division 1

1) As with mitosis, before the cell starts to divide, it <u>duplicates</u> its <u>DNA</u> — one arm of each chromosome is an <u>exact copy</u> of the other arm.

2) In the <u>first division</u> in meiosis (there are two divisions) the chromosome pairs (see previous page) <u>line up</u> in the centre of the cell.

3) They're then <u>pulled apart</u>, so each new cell only has one copy of each chromosome. <u>Some</u> of the father's chromosomes (shown in blue) and <u>some</u> of the mother's chromosomes (shown in red) go into each new cell.

4) Each new cell will have a <u>mixture</u> of the mother's and father's chromosomes. Mixing up the alleles in this way creates <u>variation</u> in the offspring. This is a huge <u>advantage</u> of <u>sexual</u> reproduction over <u>asexual</u> reproduction.

Meiosis — Division 2

5) In the <u>second division</u> the chromosomes <u>line up</u> again in the centre of the cell. It's a lot like mitosis. The arms of the chromosomes are <u>pulled apart</u>.

6) You get <u>four haploid gametes</u>, each with only a <u>single set</u> of chromosomes in it.

Relegation to the Second Division is inevitable...

Again, the best thing to do is to <u>learn the diagram</u>. Cover it up and sketch it out.

Cloning Mammals

If you've cloned a sheep before then you won't need to learn this page. If not, you'd better read on...

Cloned Mammals Can be Made by Adult Cell Cloning

Cloning is a type of asexual reproduction (see page 47). It produces cells that are genetically identical to an original cell. Here's how it's done:

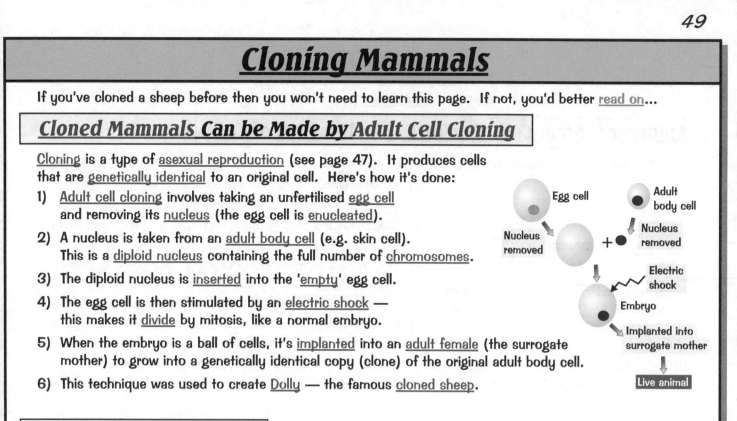

Egg cell

Nucleus removed

Adult body cell

Nucleus removed

+

Electric shock

Embryo

Implanted into surrogate mother

Live animal

1) Adult cell cloning involves taking an unfertilised egg cell and removing its nucleus (the egg cell is enucleated).

2) A nucleus is taken from an adult body cell (e.g. skin cell). This is a diploid nucleus containing the full number of chromosomes.

3) The diploid nucleus is inserted into the 'empty' egg cell.

4) The egg cell is then stimulated by an electric shock — this makes it divide by mitosis, like a normal embryo.

5) When the embryo is a ball of cells, it's implanted into an adult female (the surrogate mother) to grow into a genetically identical copy (clone) of the original adult body cell.

6) This technique was used to create Dolly — the famous cloned sheep.

Cloning Has Many Uses

1) Cloning mammals could help with the shortage of organs for transplants. For example, genetically-modified pigs are being bred that could provide suitable organs for humans. If this is successful, then cloning these pigs could help to meet the demand for organ transplants.

2) The study of animal clones could lead to greater understanding of the development of the embryo, and of ageing and age-related disorders.

3) Cloning could also be used to help preserve endangered species.

There are Many Issues Surrounding Cloning

1) Cloning mammals leads to a "reduced gene pool" — this means there are fewer different alleles in a population.

Oh Eck!

- If a population are all closely related and a new disease appears, they could all be wiped out — because there may be no allele in the population giving resistance to the disease.

2) Cloned mammals mightn't live as long — Dolly the sheep only lived for 6 years (half as long as many sheep).

- She was put down because she had lung disease, and she also had arthritis. These diseases are more usual in older sheep.

- Dolly was cloned from an older sheep, so it's been suggested her 'true' age may have been older.

- But it's possible she was just unlucky — and that her illnesses weren't linked to her being a clone.

3) There are other risks and problems associated with cloning:

- The cloning process often fails. It took hundreds of attempts to clone Dolly.

- Clones are often born with genetic defects.

- Cloned mammals' immune systems are sometimes unhealthy — so they suffer from more diseases.

Thank goodness they didn't do that with my little brother...

Cloning can be a controversial topic — especially when it's to do with cloning mammals. More large-scale, long-term studies into cloned mammals are needed to find out what the dangers are.

Stem Cells

Cells divide to make you grow. They also <u>differentiate</u> (specialise) so they can do different jobs.

Embryonic Stem Cells <u>Can Turn into Any Type of Cell</u>

1) A fertilised egg can divide by mitosis to produce a bundle of cells — the <u>embryo</u> of the new organism.

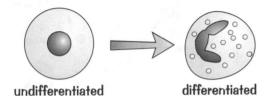

undifferentiated
stem cell

differentiated
white blood cell

2) To start with, the <u>cells</u> in the embryo are <u>all the same</u> (<u>undifferentiated</u>). They are called <u>embryonic stem cells</u>.

3) Stem cells are <u>able to divide</u> to produce either more stem cells or <u>different types</u> of <u>specialised cell</u> (e.g. blood cells).

4) The process of stem cells <u>becoming specialised</u> is called <u>differentiation</u>. It is by this process that the embryo starts to develop a recognisably human body with <u>organs</u> and <u>systems</u>.

5) In most <u>animal</u> cells, the ability to differentiate is <u>lost</u> at an early stage, but lots of <u>plant</u> cells <u>don't</u> ever lose this ability.

6) <u>Adult</u> humans only have <u>stem cells</u> in certain places like the <u>bone marrow</u>. These stem cells <u>aren't as versatile</u> as the stem cells in embryos — they can only differentiate into certain types of cell.

Stem Cells <u>May be Able to Cure Many Diseases</u>

1) Doctors already use <u>adult stem cells</u> to cure some <u>diseases</u>. E.g. <u>sickle cell anaemia</u> can sometimes be cured with a <u>bone marrow transplant</u> (containing adult stem cells which produce new blood cells).

2) Scientists have experimented with <u>extracting stem cells</u> from very early <u>human embryos</u> and <u>growing</u> them. Under certain conditions the stem cells will differentiate into <u>specialised cells</u>.

3) It <u>might</u> be possible to use stem cells to create specialised cells to <u>replace</u> those which have been <u>damaged</u> by <u>disease</u> or <u>injury</u>, e.g. new cardiac muscle cells to help someone with heart disease. This <u>potential</u> for <u>new cures</u> is the reason for the huge scientific interest in stem cells.

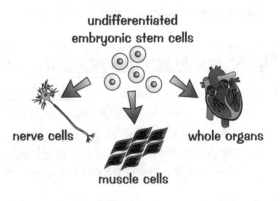

undifferentiated
embryonic stem cells

nerve cells

muscle cells

whole organs

4) Before this can happen, a lot of <u>research</u> needs to be done — and there are <u>ethical concerns</u> about this:

- Some people are strongly <u>against</u> embryonic stem cell research. They argue that human embryos <u>shouldn't</u> be used for experiments because each one is a <u>potential human life</u>. They say that scientists should find <u>other sources of stem cells</u>.
- Other people think that the aim of <u>curing patients</u> who are <u>suffering</u> should be <u>more important</u> than the potential life of the embryos. They point out that the embryos used are often <u>unwanted</u> ones from <u>fertility clinics</u> — if they weren't used for research, they would probably be <u>destroyed</u>.
- In some countries stem cell research is <u>banned</u>. It's allowed in the UK under <u>strict guidelines</u>.

But florists cell stems, and nobody complains about that...

These topics often <u>make people feel emotional</u>. Which isn't the best mindset for scientific thought... The potential of stem cells is huge — but it's early days yet. Research has recently been done into getting stem cells from <u>alternative sources</u>. For example from <u>umbilical cords</u>.

Revision Summary for B2 Topic 1

There's a lot to remember from this section and some of the topics are controversial, like cloning and genetic engineering. You need to know all sides of the story, as well as all the facts... so, here are some questions to help you figure out what you know. If you get any wrong, go back and learn the stuff.

1) Name four parts of a cell that both plants and animal cells have.
   What three things do plant cells have that animal cells don't?

2) Name four features of a cell that bacteria have.

3)* A magnified image is 7.5 mm wide. The specimen is 0.3 mm wide. What is the magnification?

4) What shape is a molecule of DNA?

5) Name the four different bases found in DNA. How do they pair up?

6) Name the four scientists who had major roles in discovering the structure of DNA.

7) What is a gene?

8) What does a triplet of DNA bases code for?

9) Describe the stages of protein synthesis.

10) Are mutations always harmful? Explain your answer.

11) Give a definition of a catalyst.

12) Name three enzyme-catalysed chemical reactions that happen inside living organisms.

13) Describe the "lock and key mechanism" of enzymes.

14) Explain why an enzyme-catalysed reaction stops when the reaction mixture is heated above a certain temperature.

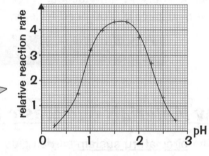

15)* The graph on the right shows how the rate of an enzyme-catalysed reaction depends on pH:
   a) State the optimum pH of the enzyme.
   b) In which part of the human digestive system would you expect to find the enzyme?

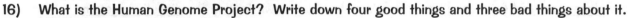

16) What is the Human Genome Project? Write down four good things and three bad things about it.

17) Describe how genetic engineering works.

18) State three useful applications of genetic engineering.

19) Why are some people concerned about genetic engineering?

20) What is mitosis used for in the human body? Describe the four stages of mitosis.

21) Where does meiosis take place in the human body?

22) How many cells are produced from an original cell when it divides by meiosis?
    Are the new cells diploid or haploid?

23) Describe the process of cloning a mammal from an adult cell (e.g. cloning a sheep).

24) Give three possible uses of cloning mammals.

25) Describe three risks associated with trying to clone mammals.

26) What is meant by the 'differentiation' of cells?

27) How are the stem cells in an embryo different from the stem cells in an adult?

28) Give an example of how embryonic stem cells could be used to cure diseases.

*Answers to these questions are given on p.108.

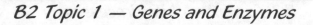

B2 Topic 1 — Genes and Enzymes

Respiration

Respiration might not sound very 'rock n roll' but it's <u>pretty fundamental</u> to life as we know it.
So roll up your sleeves, take a deep breath (sorry), and get stuck in...

Respiration *is NOT 'Breathing In and Out'*

1) <u>Respiration</u> is <u>really</u> important — it's the process used by <u>all living organisms</u> to <u>release energy</u> from <u>organic molecules</u> (usually <u>glucose</u>).

This energy is used to do things like:
* build up <u>larger molecules</u> (like proteins)
* contract <u>muscles</u> (see next page)
* maintain a steady <u>body temperature</u>

2) Respiration is how <u>all living things</u> get <u>energy</u> from <u>food</u>.

<u>RESPIRATION</u> is the process of <u>BREAKING DOWN GLUCOSE TO RELEASE ENERGY</u>, which goes on <u>IN EVERY LIVING CELL</u>

Aerobic *Respiration Needs Plenty of Oxygen*

<u>Aerobic respiration</u> is respiration using <u>oxygen</u> ('<u>aerobic</u>' just means '<u>with air</u>'). It's the most efficient way to release energy from glucose. (You can also have anaerobic respiration, which happens <u>without</u> oxygen — see next page). You need to learn the <u>word equation</u> for aerobic respiration:

Glucose + Oxygen → Carbon Dioxide + Water (+ ENERGY)

Raw Materials *and* Waste Diffuse *In and Out of Cells*

1) The <u>circulatory system</u> carries glucose, oxygen and CO_2 around the body in the <u>blood</u>.

2) The <u>glucose</u> needed for respiration comes from breaking down food in the <u>digestive system</u>.

3) The <u>oxygen</u> comes from air breathed <u>into</u> the <u>lungs</u>. CO_2 is breathed <u>out</u>.

4) The smallest blood vessels in the body are the <u>capillaries</u>. All the cells in the body have capillaries nearby to supply them with glucose and oxygen, and to take away the waste <u>carbon dioxide</u>.

5) These substances move between the cells and the capillaries by a process called <u>diffusion</u>.

6) 'Diffusion' is really simple. It's just the <u>gradual movement of particles</u> from places where there are <u>lots of them</u> to places where there are <u>fewer of them</u>. That's all it is — <u>it's just the natural tendency for stuff to spread out</u>. Unfortunately you also have to <u>learn</u> the fancy way of saying this, which is:

<u>DIFFUSION</u> is the <u>MOVEMENT OF PARTICLES</u> from an area of <u>HIGHER CONCENTRATION</u> to an area of <u>LOWER CONCENTRATION</u>

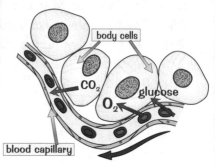

7) When cells respire they <u>use up</u> oxygen and glucose, so the concentration of these inside the cells is <u>low</u>. The concentration of these substances in the blood is <u>higher</u>, so they diffuse from the capillaries into the cells.

8) When cells respire they <u>produce</u> lots of carbon dioxide, so the concentration of this in the cells is <u>high</u>. This means carbon dioxide diffuses from the cells into the blood, where the concentration is <u>lower</u>.

9) The <u>bigger</u> the difference in concentration, the <u>faster</u> the rate of diffusion.

Revision by diffusion — you wish...

Wouldn't that be great — if all the ideas in this book would just gradually drift across into your mind, from an area of <u>high concentration</u> (in the book) to an area of <u>low concentration</u> (in your mind — no offence). Actually, that probably will happen if you read it again. Why don't you give it a go...

Respiration and Exercise

Your <u>rate of respiration</u> depends on what you're doing...

When You Exercise You Respire More

1) Muscles need <u>energy</u> from respiration to <u>contract</u>. When you exercise some of your muscles contract more frequently than normal so you need <u>more energy</u>. This energy comes from <u>increased respiration</u>.

2) The increase in respiration means you need to get <u>more oxygen</u> into the cells.

3) Your <u>breathing rate increases</u> to get more oxygen into the blood, and to get this oxygenated blood around the body faster your <u>heart rate increases</u>. This <u>removes CO_2</u> more quickly at the same time.

4) To deal with the increased demand, the rate of <u>diffusion</u> of <u>carbon dioxide</u> and <u>oxygen</u> at the <u>lung surface</u> and in <u>muscle cells</u> increases.

5) When you do <u>really vigorous exercise</u> (like sprinting) your body can't supply <u>oxygen</u> to your muscles quickly enough, so they start <u>respiring anaerobically</u>.

You need to know this equation: CARDIAC OUTPUT = HEART RATE × STROKE VOLUME

You need to be able to use it too — e.g. if you're told heart rate is <u>80</u> bpm and stroke volume is <u>70</u> cm³, cardiac output is 80 × 70 = <u>5600</u> cm³ per min.

Cardiac output is the volume of blood the heart pumps in one minute — it increases as heart rate increases.

Anaerobic Respiration Doesn't Use Oxygen At All

1) <u>Anaerobic respiration</u> happens when there's <u>not enough oxygen available</u>. <u>Anaerobic</u> just means <u>without air</u>.

2) You need to learn the overall <u>word equation</u>. ⟶ Glucose ⟶ Lactic Acid (+ ENERGY)

3) Anaerobic respiration does <u>not release as much energy</u> as aerobic respiration (but it's useful in emergencies).

4) It also produces a build-up of <u>lactic acid</u> in the muscles, which gets <u>painful</u> and can give you <u>cramp</u>.

5) The advantage is that at least you can keep on <u>using your muscles</u> for a while longer.

6) After resorting to anaerobic respiration, when you stop exercising you'll have an <u>oxygen debt</u>.

7) In other words you have to 'repay' the oxygen which you didn't manage to get to your muscles in time. The amount of oxygen required is called the <u>excess post-exercise oxygen consumption</u> (<u>EPOC</u>).

8) This means you have to <u>keep breathing hard</u> for a while <u>after you stop</u> to get more oxygen into the blood. Your <u>heart rate</u> also <u>stays high</u> to get the oxygen to your muscles, where it's used to convert the toxic <u>lactic acid</u> to harmless <u>CO_2</u> and <u>water</u>.

You Can Investigate The Effect of Exercise on Breathing and Heart Rate

1) You can measure <u>breathing rate</u> by <u>counting breaths</u>, and <u>heart rate</u> by <u>taking the pulse</u>.

2) E.g. you could take your <u>pulse</u> after:
   • <u>sitting down</u> for 5 minutes,
   • then after 5 minutes of <u>gentle walking</u>,
   • then again after 5 minutes of <u>slow jogging</u>,
   • then again after <u>running</u> for 5 minutes,
   and <u>plot</u> your results in a bar chart.

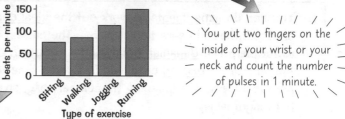

You put two fingers on the inside of your wrist or your neck and count the number of pulses in 1 minute.

3) Your pulse rate will <u>increase</u> the more <u>intense</u> the exercise is, as your body needs to get <u>more oxygen</u> to the <u>muscles</u> and take more <u>carbon dioxide away</u> from the muscles.

4) To make the experiment <u>more reliable</u>, do it as a <u>group</u> and plot the <u>average pulse rate</u> for each exercise.

Oxygen debt — cheap to pay back...

So, your heart rate and breathing rate go up when you exercise. But remember, they don't go straight back to normal when you <u>stop</u> — they'll return to normal <u>gradually</u> as your body recovers and gets the oxygen it needs.

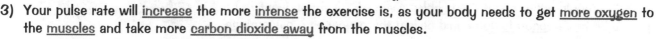

Photosynthesis

You don't know photosynthesis 'til you know its <u>equation</u>. It's in a <u>nice green box</u> so you can't possibly miss it.

Plants are Able to Make Their Own Food by Photosynthesis

1) <u>Photosynthesis</u> is the process that produces '<u>food</u>' in <u>plants</u>. The 'food' it produces is <u>glucose</u>.
2) Photosynthesis happens in the leaves of all <u>green plants</u> — this is what the leaves are for.
3) Photosynthesis happens inside the <u>chloroplasts</u>. They contain <u>chlorophyll</u>, which absorbs <u>energy</u> in <u>sunlight</u> and uses it to convert <u>carbon dioxide</u> and <u>water</u> into <u>glucose</u>. <u>Oxygen</u> is also produced as a by-product. You need to learn the equation:

$$\text{Carbon dioxide} + \text{water} \xrightarrow[\text{chlorophyll}]{\text{SUNLIGHT}} \text{glucose} + \text{oxygen}$$

Leaves are Adapted for Efficient Photosynthesis

1) Leaves are <u>broad</u>, so there's a <u>large surface area</u> exposed to <u>light</u>.
2) Leaves contain lots of <u>chlorophyll</u> in <u>chloroplasts</u> to <u>absorb light</u> (see above).
3) Leaves are full of little holes called <u>stomata</u>. They open and close to let gases like CO_2 and O_2 in and out. They also allow <u>water vapour</u> to escape — which is known as <u>transpiration</u> (see page 57).

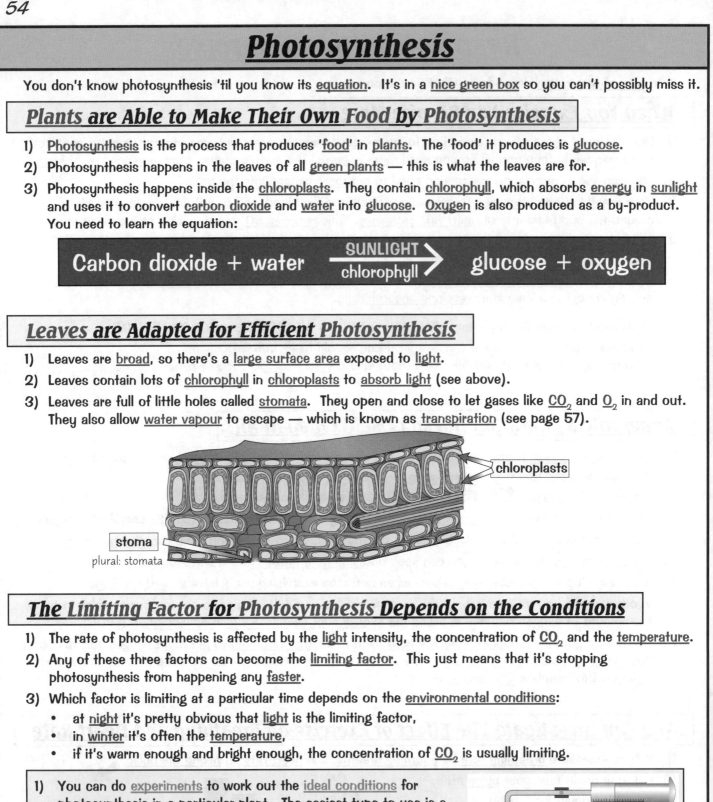

chloroplasts

stoma
plural: stomata

The Limiting Factor for Photosynthesis Depends on the Conditions

1) The rate of photosynthesis is affected by the <u>light</u> intensity, the concentration of CO_2 and the <u>temperature</u>.
2) Any of these three factors can become the <u>limiting factor</u>. This just means that it's stopping photosynthesis from happening any <u>faster</u>.
3) Which factor is limiting at a particular time depends on the <u>environmental conditions</u>:
   - at <u>night</u> it's pretty obvious that <u>light</u> is the limiting factor,
   - in <u>winter</u> it's often the <u>temperature</u>,
   - if it's warm enough and bright enough, the concentration of CO_2 is usually limiting.

1) You can do <u>experiments</u> to work out the <u>ideal conditions</u> for photosynthesis in a particular plant. The easiest type to use is a water plant like <u>Canadian pondweed</u> — you can easily measure the amount of <u>oxygen produced</u> in a given time to show how <u>fast</u> photosynthesis is happening (remember, oxygen is made during photosynthesis).

bubbles of oxygen

pondweed

2) You could either count the <u>bubbles</u> given off, or if you want to be a bit more <u>accurate</u> you could <u>collect</u> the oxygen in a <u>gas syringe</u>.
3) You can then <u>measure</u> how <u>different factors</u> affect the <u>rate of photosynthesis</u> — see the next page...

If you don't do much revision, it's time to turn over a new leaf...

Plants also need <u>water</u> for photosynthesis, but when a plant is so short of water that there's not enough for photosynthesis to take place, it's already in such <u>trouble</u> that this is the least of its worries...

The Rate of Photosynthesis

Before you start on this page, make sure you've read the photosynthesis experiment from the last page. OK...

Three Important Graphs for Rate of Photosynthesis

① Not Enough LIGHT Slows Down the Rate of Photosynthesis

1) Light provides the energy needed for photosynthesis.

2) As the light level is raised, the rate of photosynthesis increases steadily — but only up to a certain point.

3) Beyond that, it won't make any difference — it'll be either the temperature or the CO_2 level which is the limiting factor.

4) In the lab you can change the light intensity by moving a lamp closer to or further away from your plant.

5) But if you just plot the rate of photosynthesis against "distance of lamp from the beaker", you get a weird-shaped graph. To get a graph like the one above you either need to measure the light intensity at the beaker using a light meter or do a bit of nifty maths with your results.

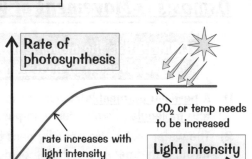

② Too Little CARBON DIOXIDE Also Slows it Down

1) CO_2 is one of the raw materials needed for photosynthesis.

2) As with light intensity the concentration of CO_2 will only increase the rate of photosynthesis up to a point. After this the graph flattens out showing that CO_2 is no longer the limiting factor.

3) As long as light and CO_2 are in plentiful supply then the factor limiting photosynthesis must be temperature.

4) There are loads of different ways to control the concentration of CO_2. E.g. dissolve different amounts of sodium hydrogencarbonate (which gives off CO_2) in the water.

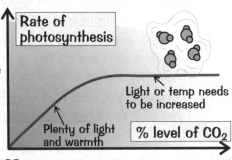

③ The TEMPERATURE has to be Just Right

1) Usually, if the temperature is the limiting factor it's because it's too low — the enzymes needed for photosynthesis work more slowly at low temperatures.

2) But if the plant gets too hot, the enzymes it needs for photosynthesis and its other reactions will be denatured (see page 44).

3) This happens at about 45 °C (pretty hot for outdoors, but greenhouses can get that hot if you're not careful).

4) Experimentally, the best way to control the temperature of the flask is to put it in a water bath.

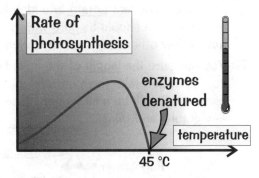

In all these experiments, you have to try and keep all the variables constant apart from the one you're investigating, so it's a fair test:

• use a bench lamp to control the intensity of the light (careful not to block the light with anything)

• keep the flask in a water bath to help keep the temperature constant

• you can't really do anything about the CO_2 levels — you just have to use a large flask, and do the experiments as quickly as you can, so that the plant doesn't use up too much of the CO_2 in the flask. If you're using sodium hydrogencarbonate make sure it's changed each time.

Don't blame it on the sunshine, don't blame it on the CO_2...

...don't blame it on the temperature, blame it on the plant. Right, and now you'll never forget the three limiting factors in photosynthesis. No... well, make sure you read these pages over and over again till you do.

Osmosis

Particles move about <u>randomly</u>, and after a bit they end up <u>evenly spaced</u>. But <u>cell membranes</u> only let some molecules, like <u>water</u>, move through. <u>Osmosis</u> is just the <u>water concentration evening up</u> across a membrane.

Osmosis is Movement of Water Molecules Across a Membrane

<u>OSMOSIS</u> is the <u>movement of water molecules</u> across a <u>partially permeable membrane</u> from a region of <u>high water concentration</u> to a region of <u>low water concentration</u>.

1) A <u>partially permeable</u> membrane is just one with very small holes in it. So small, in fact, only tiny <u>molecules</u> (like water) can pass through them, and bigger molecules (e.g. <u>sucrose</u>) can't.

2) The water molecules actually pass <u>both ways</u> through the membrane during osmosis. This happens because water molecules <u>move about randomly</u> all the time.

3) But because there are <u>more</u> water molecules on one side than on the other, there's a steady <u>net flow</u> of water into the region with <u>fewer</u> water molecules, i.e. into the <u>stronger</u> sugar solution.

4) This means the <u>strong sugar</u> solution gets more <u>dilute</u>. The water acts like it's trying to "<u>even up</u>" the concentration either side of the membrane.

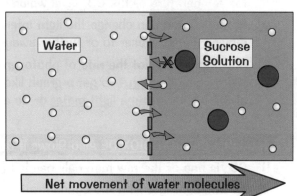

Water   Sucrose Solution

Net movement of water molecules

5) Osmosis is a special type of <u>diffusion</u> (see page 52) — passive movement of <u>water particles</u> from an area of <u>high water concentration</u> to an area of <u>low water concentration</u>.

You Can do a Practical To Show Osmosis

You can do a fairly dull practical to show osmosis at work:

1) Cut up an innocent <u>potato</u> into identical cylinders, and get some beakers with <u>different sugar solutions</u> in them. One should be <u>pure water</u>, another should be a <u>very concentrated sugar solution</u>. Then you can have a few others with concentrations <u>in between</u>.

2) You measure the <u>length</u> of the cylinders, then leave a few cylinders in each beaker for half an hour or so. Then you take them out and measure their lengths <u>again</u>. If water has moved into the cylinders by osmosis, they'll be a bit <u>longer</u>. If water has moved out, they'll have <u>shrunk</u> a bit. Then you can plot a few <u>graphs</u> and things.

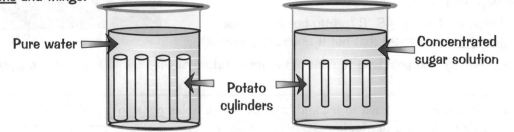

Pure water   Concentrated sugar solution

Potato cylinders

3) The <u>dependent variable</u> is the <u>chip length</u> and the <u>independent variable</u> is the <u>concentration</u> of the sugar solution. All <u>other</u> variables (volume of solution, temperature, time, type of sugar used, etc. etc.) must be kept the <u>same</u> in each case or the experiment won't be a <u>fair test</u>. See, told you it was dull.

And to all you cold-hearted potato murderers...

Cells in your body are surrounded by <u>tissue fluid</u>. It usually has a different concentration to the fluid <u>inside</u> a cell, so water either moves into or out of the cell by <u>osmosis</u>. That's why it's bad to drink <u>sea-water</u>. The high <u>salt</u> content means you end up with a much <u>lower water concentration</u> in your tissue fluid than in your cells. All the water moves out of your cells and they <u>shrivel and die</u>. So next time you're stranded at sea, remember this page.

Water Uptake and Loss in Plants

If you don't water a house plant for a few days it starts to go all droopy. Then it dies, and the people from the Society for the Protection of Plants come round and have you arrested. Plants need water.

Root Hairs Take in Water by Osmosis

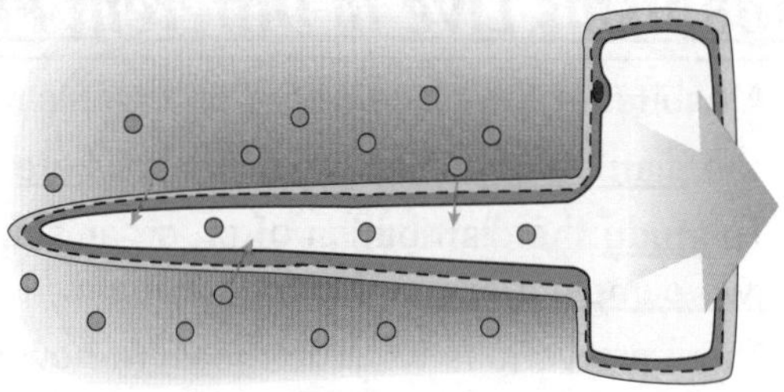

1) The cells on plant roots grow into long 'hairs' which stick out into the soil. Each branch of a root will be covered in millions of these microscopic hairs.
2) This gives the plant a big surface area for absorbing water from the soil.
3) There's usually a higher concentration of water in the soil than there is inside the plant, so the water enters the root hair cell by osmosis (see page 56).

Root Hairs Take In Minerals Using Active Transport

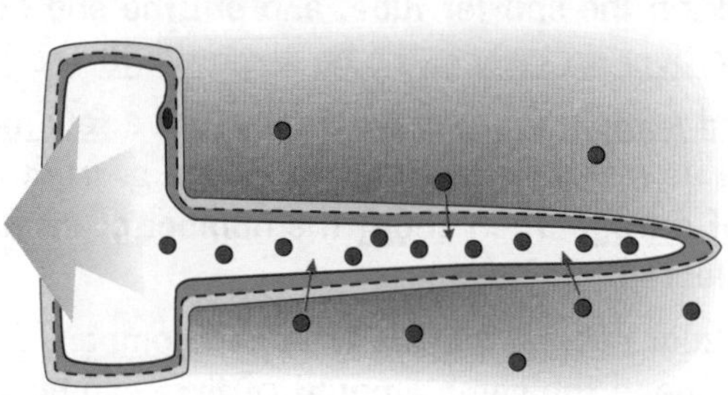

1) Root hairs also absorb minerals from the soil.
2) But the concentration of minerals in the soil is usually pretty low. It's normally higher in the root hair cell than in the soil around it.
3) So normal diffusion doesn't explain how minerals are taken up into the root hair cell.
4) The answer is that a different process called 'active transport' is responsible.
5) Active transport uses energy from respiration to help the plant pull minerals into the root hair against the concentration gradient. This is essential for its growth.

Plants have tube networks to move substances to and from individual cells quickly:
- XYLEM tubes transport water and minerals from the root to the rest of the plant (e.g. the leaves).
- PHLOEM tubes transport sugars from the leaves (where they're made) to growing and storage tissues.

Transpiration is the Loss of Water from the Plant

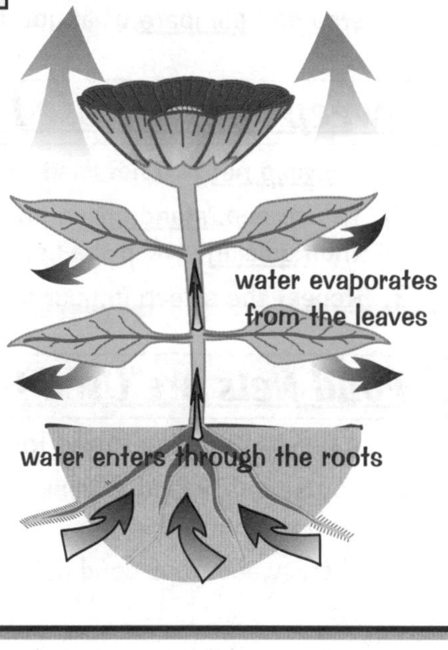

1) Transpiration is caused by the evaporation and diffusion of water from inside the leaves.
2) This creates a slight shortage of water in the leaf, and so more water is drawn up from the rest of the plant through the xylem vessels to replace it.
3) This in turn means more water is drawn up from the roots, and so there's a constant transpiration stream of water through the plant.
4) Transpiration is just a side-effect of the way leaves are adapted for photosynthesis. They have to have stomata in them so that gases can be exchanged easily (see page 54). Because there's more water inside the plant than in the air outside, the water escapes from the leaves through the stomata.
5) But, the transpiration stream does provide the plant with a constant supply of water for photosynthesis.

Transpiration — the plant version of perspiration...

A big tree loses about 1000 litres of water from its leaves every day. That's as much as an average person drinks in a year. The roots have to be very effective at drawing in water... which is why they have all those root hairs.

Distribution of Organisms

This is where the <u>fun</u> starts. Studying <u>ecology</u> gives you the chance to <u>rummage around</u> in bushes, get your hands <u>dirty</u> and look at some <u>real organisms</u>, living in the <u>wild</u>. Hold on to your hats folks...

Organisms Live in Different Places

1) A habitat is the place where an organism <u>lives</u>, e.g. a playing field.

2) The <u>distribution</u> of an organism is <u>where</u> an organism is <u>found</u>, e.g. in a part of the playing field.

3) To <u>study</u> the distribution of an organism, you can <u>measure</u> how common an organism is in <u>two sample areas</u> and compare them.

4) There are various ways to <u>measure</u> how common an organism is — you need to know about <u>five</u> of them.

(There's another one on the next page.)

Pooters Are For Collecting Ground Insects*

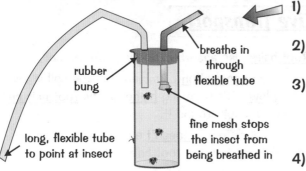

breathe in through flexible tube

rubber bung

long, flexible tube to point at insect

fine mesh stops the insect from being breathed in

1) <u>Pooters</u> are jars that have rubber bungs sealing the top, and <u>two tubes</u> stuck through the bung.

2) If you <u>suck</u> on the shorter tube, and put the end of the longer tube <u>over an insect</u>, it'll be sucked <u>into</u> the jar.

3) In your <u>first sample area</u>, crawl around for a <u>few minutes</u> sucking up as many insects as you can, e.g. from around the <u>base of a tree</u>. Then <u>count</u> the number of insects you've collected.

4) Do this in your <u>second</u> sample area and <u>compare</u> what you find. Spend the <u>same</u> amount of <u>time</u> sampling in each area, and choose sample areas of a <u>similar size</u>.

Pitfall Traps Are Another Way to Investigate Ground Insects

1) <u>Pitfall traps</u> are <u>steep-sided containers</u> that are sunk in a <u>hole</u> in the ground. The top is <u>partly open</u>.

2) Leave the trap <u>overnight</u> in your first sample area. Insects that come along <u>fall</u> into the container and <u>can't get out</u> again, so you can <u>count</u> them.

3) Then set up a pitfall trap in your second sample area and <u>compare</u> what you find.

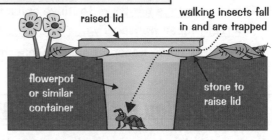

raised lid

walking insects fall in and are trapped

flowerpot or similar container

stone to raise lid

Sweep Nets Are Used For Collecting Animals From Long Grass

1) A <u>sweep net</u> is a net lined with <u>strong cloth</u> for collecting insects, spiders, etc. from <u>long grass</u>.

2) To use one, <u>stand still</u> in your first sample area and sweep the net <u>once</u> from <u>left to right</u> through the grass. Then <u>quickly</u> sweep the net up and turn the insects out into a <u>container</u> to <u>count</u> them.

3) <u>Repeat</u> the sweep in your second sample area and <u>compare</u> the numbers of organisms you find.

Pond Nets Are Used For Collecting Animals From... Ponds

1) A <u>pond net</u> is a net used for collecting insects, water snails, etc. from <u>ponds</u> and <u>rivers</u>.

2) To use one, stand in your first sample area and sweep the net <u>along the bottom</u> of the pond or river. Turn the net out into a <u>white tray</u> with a bit of water in to <u>count</u> the organisms you've caught.

3) Then sweep your pond net in your second sample area and <u>compare</u> what you find.

Traps have their pitfalls, nets have catches and pooters really suck...

For these experiments, you should <u>repeat</u> the measurements <u>several times</u> and then take the <u>average</u> result. But setting up a pitfall trap the <u>same way</u> over and over again is a lot more <u>tricky</u> than doing a regular lab experiment.

*That's insects on the ground, not some kind of powdered wasp and ant mixture.

More on the Distribution of Organisms

If this page makes no sense, turn back. Turn back a page, I mean, not abandon hope all ye who enter here...

Use a Quadrat to Study The Distribution of Small Organisms

A quadrat is a square frame enclosing a known area, e.g. 1 m². To compare how common an organism is in two sample areas, just follow these simple steps:

1) Place a 1 m² quadrat on the ground at a random point within the first sample area. E.g. divide the area into a grid and use a random number generator to pick coordinates. Otherwise, if all your samples are in one spot and everywhere else is different, the results you get won't be reproducible.

2) Count all the organisms you're interested in within the quadrat.

3) Repeat steps 1 and 2 lots of times. (The larger the sample size the better, see p.2.)

4) Work out the mean number of organisms per quadrat within the first sample area.

5) Repeat steps 1 to 4 in the second sample area.

6) Finally compare the two means. E.g. you might find 2 daisies per m² in the shade, and 22 daisies per m² (lots more) in an open field.

A quadrat

$$\text{Mean} = \frac{\text{total number of organisms}}{\text{number of quadrats}}$$

In the Exam You Might Have to Work Out Population Size

To work out the population size of an organism in one sample area:

1) Work out the mean number of organisms per m². (If your quadrat has an area of 1 m², this is the same as the mean number of organisms per quadrat, worked out above.)

2) Then multiply the mean by the total area (in m²) of the habitat.

3) E.g. if the area of an open field is 800 m², and there are 22 daisies per m², then the size of the daisy population is 22 x 800 = 17 600.

Ben liked looking after his quad-rats.

You can also find out how the distribution of an organism gradually changes across an area (e.g. from a hedge towards the middle of a field) using a belt transect:

1) Mark out a line in the area you want to study.

2) Put a quadrat down at the start of the line and count your organisms.

3) Then, instead of picking a second sample area at random, you take samples by moving your quadrat along the line, e.g. placing the quadrat at intervals of every 2 m.

transect

quadrat

You Need to Know How to Measure Environmental Factors

If you find there's a difference in the distribution of organisms, you can investigate the environmental factors that might be causing it. E.g. if you found that daisies were more common in one area than the other, you could measure the light intensity in both places. You'd probably find that the light is much brighter in the area with more daisies. One explanation could be that there are more daisies because they get more sunlight for photosynthesis (see page 54). (Careful though, you'd have to do loads more investigations to prove this.)

Here's how you can measure some environmental factors:

1) Use a thermometer to measure the temperature in different places.

2) Use an electronic device called a light sensor to measure light intensity.

3) Measure soil pH using indicator liquid — a sample of the soil is mixed with an indicator liquid that changes colour depending on the pH. The colour is compared to a chart to find out the pH of the soil. Electronic pH monitors can also be used.

Drat, drat, and double drat — my favourite use of quadrats...

You must put your quadrat down in a random place before you start counting. Anything, even chucking the quadrat over your shoulder*, is better than plonking it down right on the first big patch of organisms that you see.

*Not an invitation to break equipment or maim fellow students etc.

B2 Topic 2 — Life Processes

Revision Summary for B2 Topic 2

Hurrah. The section is almost complete. Before you move on to Topic 3, try these revision questions.
Do them all and check your answers. If you get any wrong, then learn those bits again, and do the questions
again. Keep on going until you can get all the questions right. It's a hard slog, but you've got to do it.
Otherwise all the useful facts you've just read will float away... and you'll be left with nothing but a vague
mental image of an ant in a plant pot.

1) Which of the following statements are true? (You can pick more than one.)
    a) Respiration is breathing in and out.
    b) Carbon dioxide is a product of aerobic respiration.
    c) Respiration only happens in animals.

2) Write down the word equation for aerobic respiration.

3) What is diffusion?

4) Write down the word equation for anaerobic respiration.

5) Give one advantage and one disadvantage of anaerobic respiration.

6)* Danny measured his heart rate before, during and after exercise. He plotted a graph of the results.
    Look at the graph and then answer the three questions below.

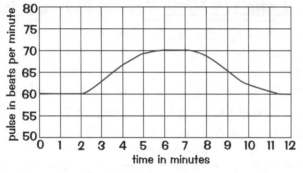

    a) What was Danny's heart rate (in beats per minute) when he was at rest?
    b) After how many minutes did Danny start exercising?
    c) What was Danny's highest heart rate?

7) What is the green substance in leaves that absorbs energy from sunlight?

8) Write down the equation for photosynthesis.

9) Name the three factors that can limit photosynthesis.

10) You carry out an experiment where you change the light intensity experienced by a piece of Canadian
    pondweed by changing the distance between the pondweed and a lamp supplying it with light.
    Write down three things which must be kept constant for this experiment to be a fair test.

11) Explain why it's important that a plant doesn't get too hot.

12) What is osmosis?

13) A solution of pure water is separated from a concentrated sugar solution by a partially permeable
    membrane. In which direction will molecules flow, and what substance will these molecules be?

14) An osmosis experiment involves placing pieces of potato into sugar solutions of various
    concentrations and measuring their lengths before and after. What is:
    a) the independent variable,
    b) the dependent variable?

15) What is the advantage to a plant of having root hairs?

16) What is transpiration?

17) Describe how you collect insects using a pooter.

18) Describe how you would investigate the distribution of organisms using a quadrat.

19) How do you measure soil pH?

*Answer to this question is given on p.108.

Evidence for Evolution

The <u>theory of evolution</u> states that more than <u>3 billion years ago</u>, life on Earth began as <u>simple organisms</u> from which all the more <u>complex organisms evolved</u> (rather than just popping into existence).

Fossils *Provide Lots of* Evidence for Evolution

1) A fossil is <u>any trace</u> of an animal or plant that lived long ago.

2) Fossils can be <u>formed</u> in three ways:

- From <u>gradual replacement</u> by minerals — things like <u>teeth</u>, <u>shells</u> and <u>bones</u> don't <u>decay</u> easily so can last ages when <u>buried</u>. They're eventually replaced by <u>minerals</u>, forming a <u>rock-like</u> substance shaped like the original hard part. The fossil stays <u>distinct</u> inside rock, and is eventually <u>dug up</u>.
- From <u>casts</u> and <u>impressions</u> — fossils can form when an organism's buried in a <u>soft material</u> like <u>clay</u>. The clay hardens around it and the organism decays, leaving a <u>cast</u> of itself. Things like <u>footprints</u> can be pressed into these materials when soft, leaving an <u>impression</u> when it hardens.
- From <u>preservation</u> in places where <u>no decay happens</u> — this is because the conditions aren't suitable for microbes to work, e.g. in <u>glaciers</u> (too cold), in <u>peat bogs</u> (too acidic) and in <u>amber</u> (no oxygen or moisture).

3) Fossils found in <u>rock layers</u> tell us <u>three things</u>:
- What the creatures and plants <u>looked like</u>.
- How <u>long ago</u> they existed. Generally, the <u>deeper</u> the rock, the <u>older</u> the fossil.
- How they've <u>evolved</u>. From studying the <u>similarities</u> and <u>differences</u> between fossils in differently aged rocks, we can see how species have <u>changed</u> and <u>developed</u> over <u>billions of years</u>. E.g. if you look at the <u>fossilised bones</u> of a <u>horse</u>, you can put together a family tree — showing how modern horse have <u>evolved</u>.

Suggested evolution of the horse

Body   Forefeet

4) The fossil record is <u>incomplete</u> (there are 'missing links'). This is because:
- <u>Very few</u> dead plants or animals actually turn into fossils. Most just <u>decay away</u>.
- Some body parts, like <u>soft tissue</u>, tend to decay away <u>completely</u>.
- There are fossils yet to be <u>discovered</u> that might help complete the picture.

The Pentadactyl Limb *Provides* Evidence for Evolution

1) A <u>pentadactyl limb</u> is a limb with <u>five digits</u>.

2) You can see the pentadactyl limb in <u>many species</u>, e.g. mammals, reptiles, amphibians.

3) In each of these species the pentadactyl limb has a <u>similar bone structure</u>, but usually a <u>different function</u>. For example, a <u>human's hand</u> and a <u>bat's wing</u> are both pentadactyl limbs — and they look pretty alike...

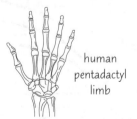

human pentadactyl limb

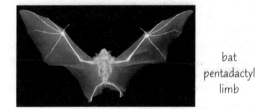

© Untitled X-Ray / Nick Veasey /Getty Images

bat pentadactyl limb

...but we can't use ours to <u>fly</u>. D'oh.

4) The <u>similarity</u> in bone structure provides <u>evidence</u> that species with a pentadactyl limb have all <u>evolved</u> from a <u>common ancestor</u> (that had a pentadactyl limb). If they'd all evolved from different ancestors, it'd be <u>highly unlikely</u> that they'd share a similar bone structure.

My brother's cleaning habits don't provide ANY evidence for evolution...

... but luckily, <u>fossils</u> do. So, you need to learn exactly how fossils and the <u>pentadactyl limb</u> provide evidence for evolution. Then, just before your brain is about to <u>overflow</u> with all that stuff, go and make yourself a cuppa.

Growth and Development

Growth — it happens to us all. You need to know how to <u>measure</u> it and the <u>processes</u> involved in both <u>animal</u> and <u>plant</u> growth. Then, just for you, there's a beauty of a <u>graph</u> at the bottom of the page. Enjoy.

Growth *is an Increase in Size or Mass*

You can <u>measure</u> the <u>growth</u> of an organism in these three ways:

1) `Size` — You can measure its <u>height</u>, <u>length</u>, <u>width</u> or <u>circumference</u>.

2) `Wet mass` — Organisms <u>contain</u> a lot of <u>water</u>. The mass of the organism depends on how much water it has gained or lost (e.g. through drinking or sweating). The <u>wet mass</u> of the organism is its mass <u>including all the water</u> in its body — it can vary a lot from <u>one day to the next</u>.

3) `Dry mass` — The <u>dry mass</u> is the mass of an organism with <u>no water in its body</u>.
This doesn't vary in the same way as wet mass, but you can only measure it once the organism's dead. The dead organism is <u>dried out</u> by leaving it in a hot oven overnight — then what's left is weighed.

Growth *Involves Cell Differentiation, Division and Elongation*

1) Plants and animals <u>grow</u> and <u>develop</u> due to these processes:
   - <u>CELL DIFFERENTIATION</u> — the process by which a cell <u>changes</u> to become <u>specialised</u> for its <u>job</u>.
   - <u>CELL DIVISION</u> — by <u>mitosis</u> (see page 47).
   - <u>CELL ELONGATION</u> — where a plant cell <u>expands</u>, making the cell <u>bigger</u> and so making the plant <u>grow</u>. It happens only in <u>plants</u>.

2) Plants and animals <u>grow differently</u>.

3) Growth in <u>animals</u> happens by <u>cell division</u>. Animals tend to grow while they're <u>young</u>, and then they reach <u>full growth</u> and <u>stop</u> growing. So when you're young, cells divide at a <u>fast rate</u> but once you're an adult, most cell division is for <u>repair</u> — the cells divide to <u>replace</u> old or damaged cells. This also means, in most animals, <u>cell differentiation</u> is <u>lost</u> at an <u>early stage</u>.

4) <u>Plants</u> often grow <u>continuously</u> — even really old trees will keep putting out <u>new branches</u>. So, plants continue to <u>differentiate</u> to <u>develop new parts</u>, e.g. leaves, roots. Growth in <u>height</u> is mainly due to cell <u>elongation</u> — cell <u>division</u> usually just happens in the <u>tips</u> of the <u>roots</u> and <u>shoots</u>.

You Need to be Able to Interpret Percentile Charts *for Growth Data*

1) <u>Growth charts</u> are used to assess a child's growth over time, so that an <u>overall pattern in development</u> can be seen and any <u>problems highlighted</u> (e.g. obesity, malnutrition, dwarfism, etc.).

2) For example, a baby's growth is regularly <u>monitored</u> after birth to make sure it's growing <u>normally</u>. Three measurements are taken — <u>length</u>, <u>mass</u> and <u>head circumference</u>.

3) These results are plotted on <u>average growth charts</u>, like this...

4) The chart shows a number of '<u>percentiles</u>'. E.g. the <u>50th percentile</u> shows the mass that <u>50%</u> of babies will have reached at a certain age.

5) Babies <u>vary</u> in size, so doctors aren't usually concerned unless a baby's size is above the <u>98th</u> percentile or below the <u>2nd</u> percentile, or if there's an <u>inconsistent pattern</u> (e.g. a small baby with a very large head).

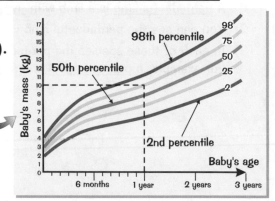

E.g. a one-year-old who weighs 10 kg is in the 75th percentile — 75% of one-year-olds are lighter and 25% are heavier. The baby is within the normal range — below the 98th percentile and above the 2nd percentile.

I'm growing rather sick of this topic...

Growth is pretty <u>important</u>. Obviously. Without it, you wouldn't be able to reach anything on the top shelf, look down your nose at someone or command respect from small children. So, now you appreciate just <u>how</u> important it is, it's time to get learning all of this stuff — yep, it's cover the page and scribble time...

Cell Organisation and the Circulatory System

Cells in <u>multicellular organisms</u> are organised. This involves a <u>to-do list</u>, a <u>diary</u> and a nice big <u>spreadsheet</u>...

Cells Make Up Tissues, Organs and Systems

Cells differentiate (see page 50) and become <u>specialised</u>. These <u>specialised cells</u> form <u>tissues</u>, which form <u>organs</u>, which form <u>organ systems</u> (see below). <u>Large multicellular organisms</u> have different <u>systems</u> inside them for <u>exchanging</u> and <u>transporting</u> materials.

TISSUES

A <u>tissue</u> (e.g. muscle tissue) is a <u>group</u> of <u>similar cells</u> that work together to carry out a particular <u>function</u>.

ORGANS

An <u>organ</u> (e.g. the heart) is a group of <u>different tissues</u> that work together to perform a particular <u>function</u>.

ORGAN SYSTEMS

An <u>organ system</u> (e.g. the circulatory system) is a <u>group of organs</u> working together to perform a particular <u>function</u>.

These tissues have a very particular function...

The Heart is Part of the Circulatory System

You need to learn this diagram of the heart with all its blummin' labels...

1) The heart has <u>four chambers</u> and <u>four major blood vessels</u> (labelled in green on the diagram).

2) The <u>right atrium</u> of the heart receives <u>deoxygenated</u> blood from the <u>body</u> (through the <u>vena cava</u>). (The plural of atrium is atria.)

3) The deoxygenated blood moves through to the <u>right ventricle</u>, which pumps it to the <u>lungs</u> (via the <u>pulmonary artery</u>).

4) The <u>left atrium</u> receives <u>oxygenated</u> blood from the <u>lungs</u> (through the <u>pulmonary vein</u>).

5) The oxygenated blood then moves through to the <u>left ventricle</u>, which pumps it out round the <u>whole body</u> (via the <u>aorta</u>).

6) The <u>left</u> ventricle has a much <u>thicker wall</u> than the <u>right</u> ventricle. It needs more <u>muscle</u> because it has to pump blood around the <u>whole body</u>, whereas the right ventricle only has to pump it to the <u>lungs</u>.

7) <u>Valves</u> prevent the <u>backflow</u> of blood.

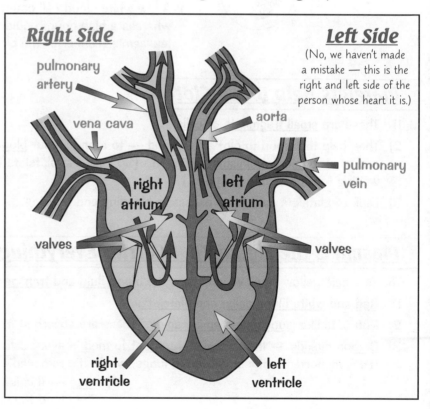

Right Side

Left Side
(No, we haven't made a mistake — this is the right and left side of the person whose heart it is.)

pulmonary artery

vena cava

aorta

right atrium

left atrium

pulmonary vein

valves

valves

right ventricle

left ventricle

Soft and quilted — the best kind of tissues...

OK, so <u>similar cells</u> are grouped together to make a <u>tissue</u>, and different tissues work together as an <u>organ</u>. Organs have a <u>particular job</u> to do in the body — e.g. the <u>heart</u> circulates blood. Groups of organs working together make up an <u>organ system</u>, like the <u>circulatory system</u>. And finally, groups of organs and organ systems working together make up a full <u>organism</u> like you or me. Phew, it's pretty complicated, this life business...

The Circulatory System — The Blood

The heart's a bit obsessed with pumping <u>blood</u> — it must be important stuff. Blood contains <u>four main things</u>...

Red Blood Cells Carry Oxygen

1) The job of red blood cells is to carry <u>oxygen</u> from the lungs to all the cells in the body.

2) They have a doughnut shape (or '<u>biconcave disc</u>' shape if you're being picky) to give a <u>large surface area</u> for absorbing <u>oxygen</u>.

3) They contain a substance called <u>haemoglobin</u>. <u>Haemoglobin</u> contains a lot of iron.

4) In the <u>lungs</u>, haemoglobin combines with <u>oxygen</u> to become <u>oxyhaemoglobin</u>. In body tissues the reverse happens to release oxygen to the <u>cells</u>.

The more red blood cells you've got, the more oxygen can get to your cells. At high altitudes there's less oxygen in the air — so people who live there produce more red blood cells to compensate.

5) Red blood cells <u>don't</u> have a nucleus — this allows more room for haemoglobin.

6) A <u>lack of iron</u> in the diet can lead to a type of <u>anaemia</u>, where the blood can't carry enough oxygen.

White Blood Cells Defend Against Disease

1) They can change shape to gobble up unwelcome <u>microorganisms</u>.

2) They produce <u>antibodies</u> to fight microorganisms, as well as <u>antitoxins</u> to neutralise any toxins produced by the microorganisms.

3) A <u>low white blood cell count</u> could increase the <u>risk of infection</u>, whereas a high count could mean you have an infection, or even leukaemia (cancer of the blood).

Platelets Help Blood Clot

1) These are <u>small fragments</u> of <u>cells</u>.

2) They help the blood to <u>clot</u> at a wound — to stop all your <u>blood pouring out</u> and to stop <u>microorganisms</u> getting in. (So basically platelets just float about waiting for accidents to happen.)

3) Lack of platelets can cause excessive bleeding and bruising.

Plasma is the Liquid That Carries Everything in Blood

This is a pale yellow liquid which keeps the blood <u>fluid</u> and <u>transports just about everything</u>:

1) <u>Red</u> and <u>white blood cells</u>, and <u>platelets</u>.

2) Nutrients like <u>glucose</u> and <u>amino acids</u>. These are absorbed from the gut and taken to body cells.

3) <u>Carbon dioxide</u> — this is a waste product formed in every cell. It's transported in the blood to the lungs, where it's removed.

4) <u>Urea</u> — this is a waste product formed in the liver. The blood transports it to the kidneys, where it's removed.

5) <u>Hormones</u> — transported from glands to target organs.

6) <u>Antibodies</u> and <u>antitoxins</u> produced by the white blood cells.

Platelets — ideal for small dinners...

When you're <u>ill</u> the doctor often takes a <u>blood sample</u> for analysis. Blood tests can be used to diagnose loads of things — <u>not</u> just disorders of the blood. This is because the blood transports <u>so many chemicals</u> produced by <u>so many organs</u>... and it's easier to take blood than, say, a piece of muscle.

The Circulatory System — Blood Vessels

The circulatory system needs <u>blood vessels</u> to <u>transport</u> the blood. It all gets a bit messy otherwise.

Blood Vessels are Designed for Their Function

There are <u>three</u> different types of <u>blood vessel</u>:

1) <u>ARTERIES</u> — these carry the blood <u>away</u> from the heart.
2) <u>CAPILLARIES</u> — these are involved in the <u>exchange of materials</u> with the tissues.
3) <u>VEINS</u> — these carry the blood <u>to</u> the heart.

Arteries Carry Blood Under Pressure

1) The heart pumps the blood out at <u>high pressure</u> so the artery walls are <u>strong</u> and <u>elastic</u>.

2) The walls are <u>thick</u> compared to the size of the hole down the middle (the "<u>lumen</u>"). They contain thick layers of <u>muscle</u> to make them <u>strong</u>.

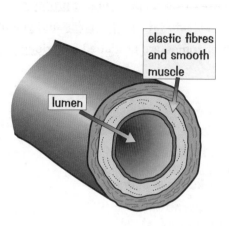

elastic fibres and smooth muscle

lumen

Capillaries are Really Small

thin wall — only one cell thick

very small lumen

nucleus of cell

1) Arteries branch into <u>capillaries</u>.
2) Capillaries are really <u>tiny</u> — too small to see.
3) They carry the blood <u>really close</u> to <u>every cell</u> in the body to <u>exchange substances</u> with them.
4) They have <u>permeable</u> walls, so substances can <u>diffuse</u> in and out.
5) They supply <u>food</u> and <u>oxygen</u>, and take away <u>wastes</u> like CO_2.
6) Their walls are usually <u>only one cell thick</u>. This <u>increases</u> the rate of diffusion by <u>decreasing</u> the <u>distance</u> over which it occurs.

Veins Take Blood Back to the Heart

1) Capillaries eventually <u>join up</u> to form <u>veins</u>.
2) The blood is at <u>lower pressure</u> in the veins so the walls don't need to be as <u>thick</u> as artery walls.
3) They have a <u>bigger lumen</u> than arteries to help the blood <u>flow</u> despite the lower pressure.
4) They also have <u>valves</u> to help keep the blood flowing in the <u>right direction</u>.

large lumen

elastic fibres and smooth muscle

Learn this page — don't struggle in vein...

Here's an interesting fact for you — your body contains about <u>60 000 miles</u> of blood vessels. That's about <u>six times</u> the distance from <u>London</u> to <u>Sydney</u> in Australia. Of course, capillaries are really tiny, which is how there can be such a big length — they can only be seen with a <u>microscope</u>.

B2 Topic 3 — Organ Systems

The Digestive System and Enzymes

Digestion is the <u>breakdown</u> of food into <u>soluble products</u>, which are then <u>absorbed</u> into the body. It happens in the <u>digestive system</u>. Here, food is broken down <u>mechanically</u> (by chewing) and by <u>digestive enzymes</u>.

The Breakdown of Food is Catalysed by Enzymes

1) <u>Starch</u>, <u>proteins</u> and <u>fats</u> are BIG molecules — too big to pass through the walls of the digestive system.

2) <u>Sugars</u>, <u>amino acids</u>, <u>glycerol</u> and <u>fatty acids</u> are much smaller molecules — they can pass easily through the walls of the digestive system.

3) The <u>digestive enzymes</u> break down the BIG molecules into the smaller ones:

- <u>Carbohydrases</u> (e.g. amylase) digest <u>starch</u> to <u>sugars</u>.
- <u>Proteases</u> (e.g. pepsin) digest <u>proteins</u> to <u>amino acids</u>.
- <u>Lipase</u> digests <u>fat</u> to <u>fatty acids</u> and <u>glycerol</u>.

Big molecules like starch are <u>insoluble</u> (don't dissolve in water). They're broken down into smaller molecules like sugars, which are <u>soluble</u> (do dissolve in water).

4) Digestive enzymes are produced in <u>various places</u> in your digestive system...

MOUTH

1) Food is <u>moistened</u> with <u>saliva</u> from the <u>salivary glands</u>.

2) The <u>salivary glands</u> produce <u>amylase enzyme</u> in the <u>saliva</u>, which breaks down starch.

3) Food is <u>chewed</u> to form a <u>ball of food</u> (<u>bolus</u>), before being <u>swallowed</u>.

Tongue

OESOPHAGUS

A tube that takes food from the <u>mouth</u> to the <u>stomach</u>. It's lined with <u>muscles</u> that <u>contract</u> to help the ball of food move along, by <u>peristalsis</u> (see page 68).

LIVER

Where <u>bile</u> is <u>produced</u>. Bile <u>neutralises stomach acid</u> and <u>emulsifies fats</u> (see page 68).

GALL BLADDER

Where <u>bile</u> is <u>stored</u>, before it's released into the <u>small intestine</u>.

STOMACH

1) It <u>pummels</u> the food with its muscular walls.

2) It produces the <u>protease</u> enzyme, <u>pepsin</u>.

3) It produces <u>hydrochloric acid</u> for two reasons:
   a) To <u>kill bacteria</u>
   b) To give the <u>right pH</u> for the <u>protease</u> enzyme to work (pH 2 — <u>acidic</u>).

SMALL INTESTINE

1) Produces <u>protease</u>, <u>amylase</u> and <u>lipase</u> enzymes to complete digestion.

2) This is also where the "food" is <u>absorbed</u> out of the digestive system into the body.

PANCREAS

Produces <u>protease</u>, <u>amylase</u> and <u>lipase</u> enzymes. It releases these into the <u>small intestine</u>.

LARGE INTESTINE

Where <u>excess water</u> is <u>absorbed</u> from the food.

Mmmm — so who's for a chocolate digestive...

Your <u>digestive system</u> gets loads of <u>food</u> piled into it. Sometimes though, I manage to miss my mouth and the food falls on my shirt. Luckily, some clever clogs thought of using <u>enzymes</u> in <u>washing powder</u>. They break down the big, insoluble molecules to smaller, soluble ones — so the mess on my shirt is washed away in water. <u>Genius</u>.

Investigating Digestive Enzymes

You can investigate the effect of <u>different concentrations</u> of a digestive enzyme on its substrate.
E.g. you can look at the effect of <u>amylase</u> concentrations on the digestion of <u>starch</u>. You do it like this...

Use Visking Tubing to Model the Gut

1) Visking tubing is a <u>good model</u> for the gut because, like the gut, it only lets <u>small molecules</u> through and not <u>big molecules</u>. It's also a lot <u>cheaper</u>, <u>easier</u> and <u>less yukky</u> than using an animal's gut.

2) However, visking tubing <u>isn't</u> exactly the <u>same</u> as your gut. For example, your gut's a lot <u>longer</u> and has a <u>massive surface area</u> — so the speed of digestion and absorption will be slightly <u>different</u>.

3) So visking tubing is not an <u>exact</u> model, but it's <u>good enough</u> to see how digestive enzymes work.

Use Iodine to Test for Starch and Benedict's to Test for Sugar

So let the fun (and the experiment) begin...

1) Add the <u>same volume</u> of <u>starch suspension</u> and <u>0.25% amylase solution</u> to the visking tubing, then <u>rinse</u> the outside of the tubing under a tap.

2) Put the visking tubing into a <u>boiling tube</u> with <u>distilled water</u> in it.

3) <u>Straight away</u> test a drop of <u>water</u> from around the visking tubing with <u>iodine solution</u> (see p.43), and take 5 drops to test with <u>Benedict's reagent</u> (see below). Record the <u>colour</u> each time.

distilled water — *take a drop of water*

boiling tube — *visking tubing containing amylase and starch solution*

USING BENEDICT'S REAGENT: Add 5 drops of water into a test tube. Add a drop of Benedict's reagent and put the test tube into a beaker of boiling water. Record the colour after 2-3 minutes.

blue → green → yellow → orange → brick-red

Benedict's reagent starts off blue and will change colour if there's any sugar present.
The more sugar there is, the further the colour change goes towards brick-red.

Remember to keep everything except the amylase concentration <u>constant</u>, e.g. starch concentration.

4) Leave the boiling tube for <u>15 minutes</u>.

5) Then test the water again with <u>iodine solution</u> and <u>Benedict's reagent</u>. Record the <u>colour</u> each time.

6) <u>Repeat</u> the experiment using <u>other concentrations</u> of the amylase solution, e.g. 0.5%, 1.0%, 1.5%, 2.0%.

Enzyme Concentration Affects the Rate of Reaction Up to a Point

You might get <u>results</u> a bit like this...

Amylase concentration	Colour of iodine solution		Colour of Benedict's reagent	
	start of experiment	end of experiment	start of experiment	end of experiment
0.25%	orangey-brown	orangey-brown	blue	yellow
0.5%	orangey-brown	orangey-brown	blue	orange
1%	orangey-brown	orangey-brown	blue	brick-red

1) The <u>orangey-brown</u> colour of iodine shows that <u>no starch</u> is ever present in the water. This is because the starch molecules are <u>too big</u> to pass through the visking tubing into the water.

2) The colour change of the Benedict's reagent <u>from blue</u> shows that <u>sugar</u> is present in the water. This is because <u>starch</u> has been <u>broken down</u> by <u>amylase</u> to <u>sugar</u> in the visking tubing, and the sugar molecules are <u>small enough</u> to pass through the membrane into the water.

3) The <u>higher</u> the concentration of <u>amylase</u>, the <u>further</u> the Benedict's reagent has changed colour. This means lots <u>more starch</u> has been broken down to sugar. This is because at a <u>higher concentration</u> of amylase there are <u>more active sites</u> available to break down the starch into sugar, so the starch is broken down at a <u>faster rate</u>. But above a <u>certain amylase concentration</u> the reaction <u>won't</u> get any faster because there are already <u>enough active sites</u> to deal with all the starch. This is shown on the graph:

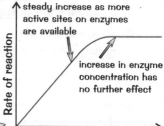

steady increase as more active sites on enzymes are available

increase in enzyme concentration has no further effect

Rate of reaction (y-axis) / *Enzyme concentration* (x-axis)

I think MY concentration has reached it's maximum amount...

This is a fairly <u>grim</u> experiment, but at least you get some <u>pretty colours</u>. Learn all of this page in all its glory.

More on Digestion

Some parts of the digestive system are rather specialised. Check out these three lovely features...

Peristalsis Involves Longitudinal and Circular Muscles

1) There's muscular tissue all the way down the digestive system — there are:
   - longitudinal muscles down the length of the gut, and
   - circular muscles running in circles around the gut.
2) The job of these muscles is to squeeze the food along. This squeezing action is called peristalsis.
3) Waves of circular muscle contractions push the food along the gut.
4) Waves of longitudinal muscle contractions run slightly ahead to help keep the food in a ball.

The gut is also called the alimentary canal.

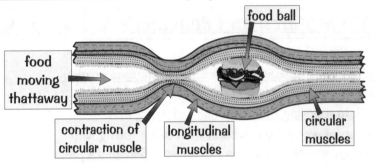

food ball

food moving thattaway

contraction of circular muscle

longitudinal muscles

circular muscles

Bile Neutralises the Stomach Acid and Emulsifies Fats

1) As you know, bile is produced in the liver and stored in the gall bladder before it's released into the small intestine (see page 66).
2) The hydrochloric acid in the stomach makes the pH too acidic for enzymes in the small intestine to work properly. Bile is alkaline — it neutralises the acid and makes conditions alkaline. The enzymes in the small intestine work best in these alkaline conditions.
3) It emulsifies fats. In other words it breaks the fat into tiny droplets. This gives a much bigger surface area of fat for the enzyme lipase to work on — which makes its digestion faster.

Villi Provide a Really Really Big Surface Area

The inside of the small intestine is covered in millions and millions of these tiny little projections called villi. Villi have three features that make absorbing digested food into the bloodstream really efficient:

1) They have a big surface area so that digested food is absorbed much more quickly into the blood.
2) They have a single layer of surface cells so that digested food diffuses quickly over a short distance.
3) They have a very good blood supply via a capillary network to assist quick absorption of digested food.

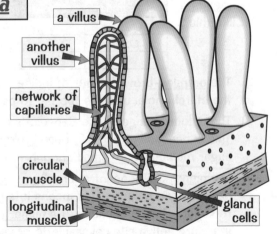

a villus

another villus

network of capillaries

circular muscle

longitudinal muscle

gland cells

You don't have to bust a gut to revise this page...

Living organisms are really well adapted for getting the substances they need to their cells. It makes sense — if they couldn't do this well, they'd die out. A large surface area is a key way that organisms' exchange surfaces are made more effective — molecules can only diffuse through a membrane when they're right next to it, and a large surface area means loads more molecules are close to the membrane. Brilliant.

Functional Foods

Welcome to the page where I say, "Don't worry, not all bacteria are bad" — yep, there are even some good ones out there (well, in there really — your gut). Some people say they're friendly, but I wouldn't go that far. It's not like they offer you a cup of tea or anything. They just help you out with a bit of digestion, that's all.

Functional Foods are Marketed as Having Health Benefits

A functional food is one that has some kind of health benefit beyond basic nutrition. For example, it might prevent some kind of disease, or it might (as the marketing folk may put it) 'promote your well-being'. You need to know about the following three foods.

Probiotics Contain 'Good' Bacteria

1) Probiotics are live bacteria, such as *Bifidobacteria* and *Lactobacillus* (a lactic acid bacterium). These 'good bacteria' are similar to those that are found naturally in your gut.
2) Probiotics are added to foods like yogurt, soya milk and dietary supplements (e.g. capsules). The bacteria may have already been there or they're added by the manufacturer.
3) It's thought that they help to keep your digestive system healthy and your immune system strong.

Prebiotics Promote the Growth of 'Good' Bacteria

1) Prebiotics are carbohydrates that we can't digest, e.g. oligosaccharides.
2) They occur naturally in foods like leeks, onions and oats, but you can't get enough of them in a normal diet to cause a significant effect. So some people take supplements containing prebiotics.
3) Prebiotics are a food supply for 'good' bacteria that are already in your digestive system. It's thought that taking prebiotics can help promote the growth of the 'good' bacteria in the gut, which in turn could improve the health of your digestive system and may also help to strengthen your immune system.

Plant Stanol Esters Reduce Cholesterol

1) Plant stanol esters are chemicals that can lower blood cholesterol and reduce the risk of heart disease.
2) Stanols occur naturally in plants, but in very small quantities. Stanols are produced commercially by using bacteria to convert sterols (types of fat found in plants like the soya bean) into stanols.
3) Some food manufacturers add them to spreads and some dairy products. People who are worried about their blood cholesterol levels may choose these spreads over normal spreads.

Not All Health Claims are Scientifically Proven

As you now know, functional foods claim they have certain health benefits. But how do you know they work... Well, when looking at evidence, it's a good idea to watch out for these things:

- Is the report a scientific study, published in a reputable journal?
- Was it written by a qualified person (not connected with the people selling it)?
- Was the sample of people asked/tested large enough to give reliable results?
- Have there been other studies which found similar results?

A "yes" to one or more of these is a good sign.

E.g. A study published in The New England Journal of Medicine provided evidence that plant stanols lower blood cholesterol. The study was in reputable journal and there have been other studies that have found similar results. Both of these things increase the reliability of the study.

While you're in there, make yourself useful...

Don't get functional foods mixed up — probiotics are bacteria you eat to 'top up' the bacteria in your gut. Prebiotics are non-digestable carbohydrates that feed the 'good' bacteria. And stanols are all about cholesterol.

Revision Summary for B2 Topic 3

And where do you think you're going? It's no use just reading through and thinking you've got it all — this stuff will only stick in your head if you've learnt it <u>properly</u>. And that's what these questions are for.

I won't pretend they'll be easy — they're not meant to be, but all the information's in the section somewhere. Have a go at all the questions, then if there are any you can't answer, go back, look stuff up and try again. Enjoy...

1) What is a fossil?
2) Explain how the pentadactyl limb provides evidence for evolution.
3) Give three ways that the growth of an organism can be measured.
4) What is cell differentiation?
5) What is a tissue? What about an organ?
6) Name one organ system found in the human body.
7) Name the blood vessel that takes blood from the right ventricle of the heart. Where does it take the blood?
8) Why does the left ventricle have a thicker wall than the right ventricle?
9) What do you call the stuff in red blood cells that makes them red and carries oxygen?
10) List three things that white blood cells do to help defend our bodies against disease.
11) What are the cell fragments called that help blood to clot? Why is it important that blood can clot?
12) What substances get carried around the body in plasma?
13) Why do arteries need very muscular, elastic walls?
14) Explain how capillaries are adapted to their function.
15) What does amylase do?
16) What two products does lipase break down fat into?
17) Describe three functions of the stomach.
18) What is the main function of the small intestine?
19) In a digestive enzyme experiment, what could you use to model the gut?
20) Describe how you can you test if starch is present in a solution.
21) Sketch a graph to show how enzyme concentration affects the rate of a reaction.
22) Give two functions of bile.
23) How does the structure of a villus make it good at its job?
24) Name two types of bacteria that a probiotic food might contain.
25) What are prebiotics? Why might some people choose to take them as a supplement?
26) Why are plant stanol esters added to spreads?
27) Give four things you should look out for when deciding whether a health claim about a functional food is true or not.

The Kidneys

Cell metabolism (<u>chemical reactions</u> in <u>cells</u>) produces <u>waste products</u> like <u>urea</u> and <u>carbon dioxide</u>. They end up in the <u>blood</u> and have to be <u>removed</u> somehow. Here's how the <u>kidneys</u> help to get rid of urea...

The Kidneys are Excretion Organs

The <u>kidneys</u> perform <u>three main roles</u>:

1) <u>Removal of urea</u> from the blood. Urea is produced in the <u>liver</u> from the breakdown of <u>excess amino acids</u>.

2) <u>Adjustment of ion levels</u> in the blood.

3) <u>Adjustment of water content</u> of the blood.

They do this by <u>filtering</u> stuff out of the blood under <u>high pressure</u>, and then <u>reabsorbing</u> the useful things. The end product is <u>urine</u>.

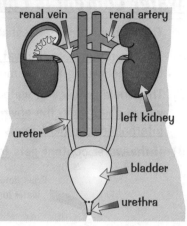

renal vein   renal artery

left kidney

ureter

bladder

urethra

Nephrons are the Filtration Units in the Kidneys

1) Ultrafiltration:

1) A <u>high pressure</u> is built up which squeezes <u>water</u>, <u>urea</u>, <u>ions</u> and <u>glucose</u> out of the blood and into the <u>Bowman's capsule</u>.

2) The <u>glomerulus</u> and the Bowman's capsule act like <u>filters</u>, so <u>big</u> molecules like <u>proteins</u> and <u>blood cells</u> are <u>not</u> squeezed out. They stay in the blood.

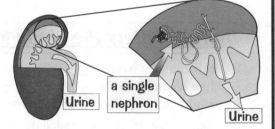

Urine

a single nephron

Urine

2) Reabsorption:

As the liquid flows along the nephron, <u>useful</u> substances are <u>reabsorbed</u>:

1) <u>All</u> the <u>glucose</u> is <u>selectively</u> reabsorbed — it's moved out of the nephron back into the blood <u>against</u> the concentration gradient.

2) <u>Sufficient water</u> is reabsorbed, according to the level of the hormone <u>ADH</u> (see next page). The process of maintaining the right water content in the body is called <u>osmoregulation</u>.

3) Release of wastes:

Urea and excess water are not reabsorbed. They continue out of the <u>nephron</u>, into the ureter and down to the <u>bladder</u> as <u>urine</u>. Urine is released through the <u>urethra</u>.

Enlarged View of a Single Nephron

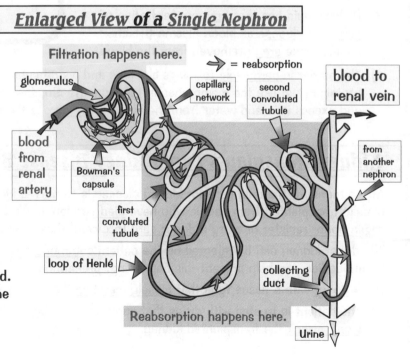

Filtration happens here.

glomerulus

⇒ = reabsorption

capillary network

second convoluted tubule

blood to renal vein

blood from renal artery

Bowman's capsule

from another nephron

first convoluted tubule

loop of Henlé

collecting duct

Reabsorption happens here.

Urine

Reabsorb those facts and excrete the excess...

On average, the kidneys filter 1500 litres of blood a day (you only have 4-6 litres of blood in your body — it just goes through the kidneys about <u>300 times</u>). And the kidneys excrete 1.5 litres of urine a day — so that's about 547.5 litres of wee a year... that's five baths full... not that I'm suggesting you try to actually fill up five baths.

More on The Kidneys

Your kidneys have a clever way of regulating water content. But problems occur when the kidneys don't work.

Water Content is Controlled by a Negative Feedback System

1) The amount of water reabsorbed in the kidney nephrons is controlled by anti-diuretic hormone (ADH).

2) The brain monitors the water content of the blood and instructs the pituitary gland to release ADH into the blood according to how much is needed.

3) The whole process of water content regulation is controlled by a mechanism called negative feedback, where changes in the environment trigger a response that counteracts the changes. This means that the internal environment tends to stay around a norm, the level at which the cells work best.

4) If the water content gets too high or too low, negative feedback brings it back to normal:

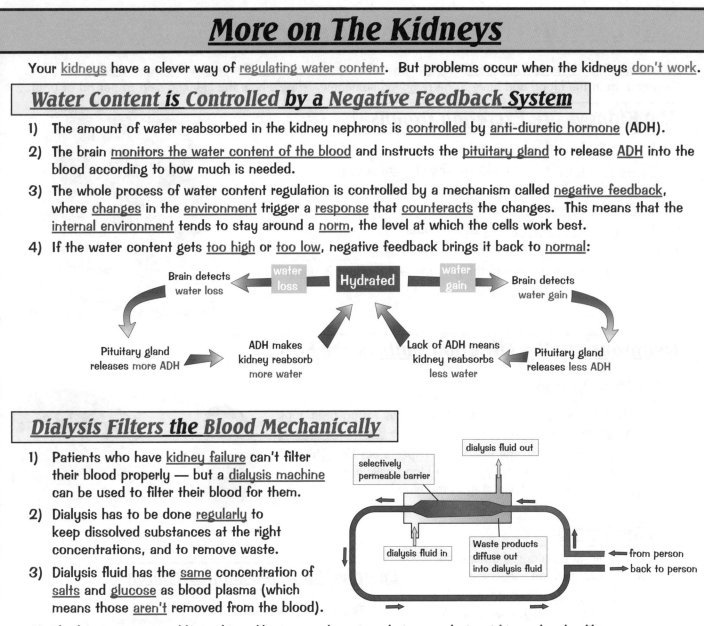

Dialysis Filters the Blood Mechanically

1) Patients who have kidney failure can't filter their blood properly — but a dialysis machine can be used to filter their blood for them.

2) Dialysis has to be done regularly to keep dissolved substances at the right concentrations, and to remove waste.

3) Dialysis fluid has the same concentration of salts and glucose as blood plasma (which means those aren't removed from the blood).

4) The barrier is permeable to things like ions and waste substances, but not big molecules like proteins (just like the membranes in the kidney). So, the waste substances (such as urea) and excess ions and water from the blood move across the membrane into the dialysis fluid.

Kidney Transplants Cure Kidney Disease But Can Be Rejected

At the moment, the only cure for kidney disease is to have a kidney transplant. Healthy kidneys are usually transplanted from people who have died suddenly, say in a car accident, and who are on the organ donor register or carry a donor card (provided their relatives give the go-ahead).

The donor kidney can be rejected by the patient's immune system — treated like a foreign body and attacked by antibodies. To help prevent this happening, precautions are taken:

1) A donor with a tissue type that closely matches the patient is chosen.

2) The patient is treated with drugs that suppress the immune system, so that their immune system won't attack the transplanted kidney.

Simon says touch urea... actually don't...

Kidney dialysis machines are expensive things for the NHS to run — and dialysis is not a pleasant experience. Transplants can put an end to the hours spent on dialysis, but there are long waiting lists for kidneys. Even if one with a matching tissue type is found, there's the possibility that it'll be rejected. And taking drugs that suppress the immune system means the person is vulnerable to other illnesses.

Reproductive Cells and The Menstrual Cycle

Fertilisation occurs when a sperm fuses with an egg. The monthly release of an egg from a woman's ovaries and the build-up and breakdown of the lining in the uterus is called the menstrual cycle.

Sperm Cells and Eggs Are Specialised for Reproduction

Eggs and sperm both have special features:

The main functions of an egg are to carry the female DNA and to nourish the developing embryo in the early stages.

Size of sperm in relation to the ovum

1) The egg contains nutrients in the cytoplasm to feed the embryo.
2) Straight after fertilisation (when a sperm fuses with the egg), the egg's membrane changes its structure to stop any more sperm getting in. This makes sure the offspring end up with the right amount of DNA.
3) The egg contains a haploid nucleus. This is so that when the egg is fertilised, the resulting cell will have the right number of chromosomes.

The function of a sperm is to transport the male's DNA to the female's egg so that their DNA can combine.

1) Sperm are small and have long tails so they can swim to the egg.
2) Sperm have lots of mitochondria in their middle section to provide the energy (from respiration) needed to swim this distance.
3) Sperm also have an acrosome at the front of the 'head', where they store the enzymes they need to digest their way through the membrane of the egg cell.
4) Sperm contain a haploid nucleus — this means that they only have one copy of each chromosome.

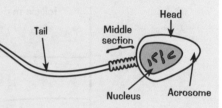

The Menstrual Cycle Has Four Stages

Stage 1 Day 1 is when the bleeding starts. The uterus lining breaks down and is released (menstruation).

Stage 2 The lining of the uterus builds up again, from day 4 to day 14, into a thick spongy layer of blood vessels ready to receive a fertilised egg.

Stage 3 An egg is released from the ovary (ovulation) at about day 14.

Stage 4 The lining is then maintained for about 14 days, until day 28. If no fertilised egg has landed on the uterus wall by day 28 then the spongy lining starts to break down again and the whole cycle starts over.

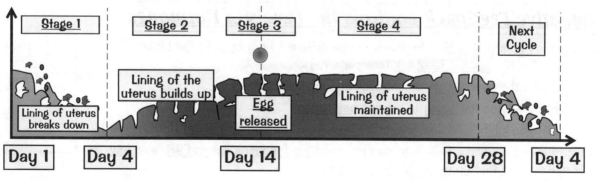

No sniggering in the back, please...

For many kids in year seven, the mere sight of a sperm is enough to convulse them in giggles. Those of them that don't think it's an innocent tadpole, anyway. But that's not the case for you lot. We hope.

Menstrual Hormones

You need to know all about the <u>cunning system</u> controlling the hormones in the menstrual cycle — lucky you...

The Menstrual Cycle is Controlled by Four Hormones

1 FSH (follicle-stimulating hormone)

1) Causes a <u>follicle</u> (an <u>egg</u> and its surrounding cells) to <u>mature</u> in one of the ovaries.
2) Stimulates <u>oestrogen</u> production.

2 Oestrogen

1) Causes the lining of the uterus to <u>thicken</u> and <u>grow</u>.
2) A high level stimulates an <u>LH surge</u> (a rapid increase).

3 LH (luteinising hormone)

1) The LH surge stimulates <u>ovulation</u> at day 14 — the follicle ruptures and the <u>egg is released</u>.
2) Stimulates the <u>remains</u> of the <u>follicle</u> to develop into a structure called a <u>corpus luteum</u> — which secretes <u>progesterone</u>.

4 Progesterone

1) <u>Maintains</u> the lining of the uterus.
2) <u>Inhibits</u> (prevents) the production of <u>FSH</u> and <u>LH</u>.
3) When the level of progesterone <u>falls</u>, and there's a low oestrogen level, the uterus lining <u>breaks down</u>.
4) A <u>low</u> progesterone level allows <u>FSH</u> to <u>increase</u>... and then the whole cycle starts again.

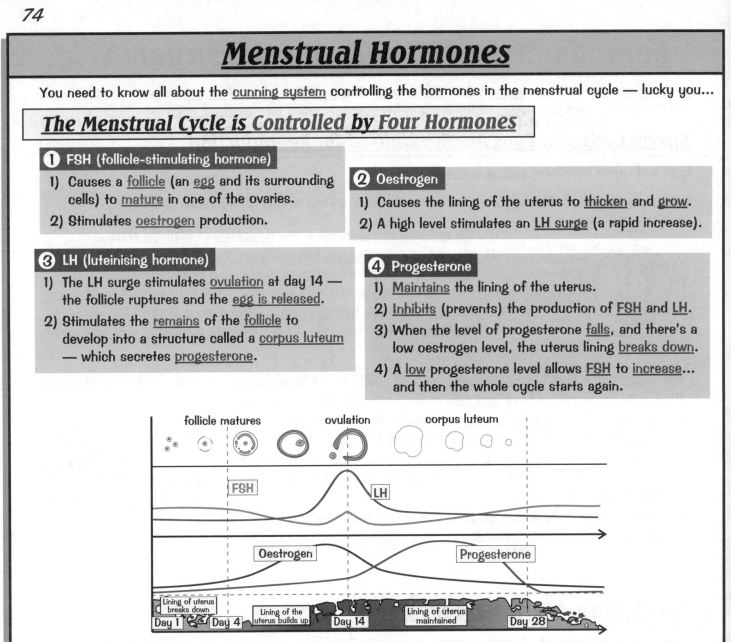

If a fertilised egg implants in the uterus (i.e. the woman becomes <u>pregnant</u>) then the level of <u>progesterone</u> will <u>stay high</u> to maintain the lining of the uterus during pregnancy.

The uterus lining has a thick spongy layer of <u>blood vessels</u> — this blood supply allows the <u>placenta</u> to develop. The placenta supplies the baby with the <u>oxygen</u>, <u>glucose</u> and <u>nutrients</u> it needs to grow, and removes its <u>waste products</u> (like <u>urea</u> and <u>carbon dioxide</u>).

Negative Feedback Controls the Levels of Hormones

During the <u>menstrual cycle</u>, the levels of the different <u>hormones</u> in the blood are controlled by <u>negative feedback</u> (see page 72).

For example, the level of <u>FSH</u> is controlled by negative feedback:

1) FSH stimulates the <u>ovary</u> to release <u>oestrogen</u>.
2) Oestrogen <u>inhibits</u> further release of <u>FSH</u> from the <u>pituitary gland</u> (in the brain).

After FSH has caused a follicle to mature, <u>negative feedback</u> keeps <u>FSH</u> level <u>low</u>. This makes sure that <u>no more follicles mature</u>.

There will be no joke on this page. There is NOTHING funny about the menstrual cycle.*

It's a good idea to get your head around that <u>diagram</u> up there — make sure you know which hormones cause:
a) a follicle to mature, b) the uterus lining to thicken, c) egg release, and d) the maintenance of the uterus lining.

Fertility Treatments

Sometimes couples who can't conceive naturally seek medical treatment to help nature along a bit.

Hormones Can Be Used To Increase Fertility

1) Some women have levels of <u>FSH</u> that are <u>too low</u> to cause their <u>eggs to mature</u>.
   This means that <u>no eggs</u> are <u>released</u> and the women <u>can't get pregnant</u>.

2) The hormones <u>FSH</u> and <u>LH</u> can be injected by these women to stimulate <u>egg release</u> in their <u>ovaries</u>.

PROS	CONS
It helps a lot of women to <u>get pregnant</u> when previously they couldn't... pretty obvious.	1) It <u>doesn't always work</u> — some women may have to do it many times, which can be <u>expensive</u>. 2) <u>Too many eggs</u> could be stimulated, resulting in unexpected <u>multiple pregnancies</u> (twins, triplets etc.).

IVF Can Help Couples to Have Children

1) <u>IVF</u> ("*in vitro* fertilisation") involves collecting <u>eggs</u> from the woman's ovaries and fertilising them in a <u>lab</u> using the man's <u>sperm</u>. These are then grown into <u>embryos</u>.

2) Once the embryos are <u>tiny balls of cells</u>, one or two of them are <u>transferred</u> to the woman's uterus (womb) to improve the chance of <u>pregnancy</u>.

3) <u>FSH</u> and <u>LH</u> are given before egg collection to <u>stimulate egg production</u> (so more than one egg can be collected).

PRO Fertility treatment can give an infertile couple <u>a child</u> — a pretty obvious <u>benefit</u>.

CONS
1) Some women have a strong <u>reaction</u> to the hormones — e.g. <u>abdominal pain</u>, <u>vomiting</u>, <u>dehydration</u>.
2) There have been some reports of an <u>increased risk of cancer</u> due to the hormonal treatment (though others have reported <u>no such risk</u> — the position isn't really clear at the moment).
3) <u>Multiple births</u> can happen if more than one embryo grows into a baby — these are <u>risky</u> for the mother and babies (there's a higher risk of miscarriage, stillbirth...).

IVF Can be Done With Donated Eggs

Women who <u>can't produce eggs</u> can use <u>eggs from a donor</u> and have <u>IVF</u> to conceive.

PROS
1) Fairly obviously... it allows a woman who can't produce eggs to have a baby.
2) Using donated eggs can <u>prevent</u> the risk of passing on a <u>genetic disorder</u> from the mother.

CON It can be <u>emotionally difficult</u> for the <u>family</u> knowing that the child has a <u>different</u> genetic mother.

A Surrogate Mother Carries A Baby For Another Couple

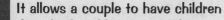

1) If a woman can't become pregnant she may ask <u>another woman</u> to carry a baby for her. The woman who carries the baby is known as a <u>surrogate mother</u>.

2) <u>IVF</u> is used to produce an <u>embryo</u>, either using an egg and sperm <u>from the couple</u> or <u>donor egg and sperm</u>. The embryo is then <u>implanted</u> into the surrogate mother's uterus.

3) After giving <u>birth</u>, the woman <u>gives</u> the baby to the <u>couple</u> who asked her to be their surrogate.

PRO	CON
It allows a couple to have children if medical problems mean the mother <u>can't become pregnant</u> or it's <u>risky</u> for her to <u>give birth</u>.	The surrogate mother is <u>legally</u> the <u>mother</u> of the child until it is <u>adopted</u> by the intended couple. She has the <u>right</u> to <u>keep</u> the child — so she might decide that she <u>doesn't</u> want to give it away.

What's an IVF surgeon's favourite drink — fertili-tea...

Around 15 000 babies are born in the UK by IVF every year. Wow. Fortunately, there are only a few pros and cons to remember for each type of treatment on this page, so turn the page over and try to write them all out.

X and Y Chromosomes

Now for a couple of very important little chromosomes...

Your Chromosomes Control Whether You're Male or Female

There are 22 matched pairs of chromosomes in every human body cell. The 23rd pair are labelled XX or XY. They're the pair of chromosomes that decide whether you turn out male or female.

> All men have an X and a Y chromosome: XY
> The Y chromosome causes male characteristics.
>
> All women have two X chromosomes: XX
> The XX combination allows female characteristics to develop.

X-chromosome

Y-chromosome

When making sperm, the X and Y chromosomes are drawn apart in the first division in meiosis. There's a 50% chance each sperm cell gets an X-chromosome and a 50% chance it gets a Y-chromosome.

A similar thing happens when making eggs. But the original cell has two X-chromosomes, so all the eggs have one X-chromosome.

Genetic Diagrams Show the Possible Combinations of Gametes

To find the probability of getting a boy or a girl, you can draw a genetic diagram.

Put the possible gametes from one parent down the side, and those from the other parent along the top. Then in each middle square you fill in the letters from the top and side that line up with that square. The pairs of letters in the middle show the possible combinations of the gametes.

There are two XX results and two XY results, so there's the same probability of getting a boy or a girl.

Don't forget that this 1:1 ratio is only a probability. If you had four kids they could all be boys — yes I know, terrifying isn't it...

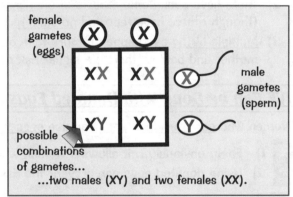

female gametes (eggs)

male gametes (sperm)

possible combinations of gametes...

...two males (XY) and two females (XX).

The other type of genetic diagram looks a bit more complicated, but it shows exactly the same thing. At the top are the parents.

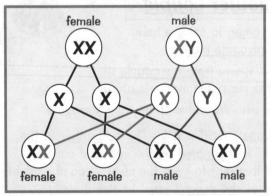

female   male

female   female   male   male

The middle circles show the possible gametes that are formed. One gamete from the female combines with one gamete from the male (during fertilisation).

The criss-cross lines show all the possible ways the X and Y chromosomes could combine. The possible combinations of the offspring are shown in the bottom circles.

Remember, only one of these possibilities would actually happen for any one offspring.

Have you got the Y-factor...

Most genetic diagrams you'll see in exams concentrate on a gene, instead of a chromosome. But the principle's the same. Don't worry — just draw them out for yourself and make sure you can follow the working through.

Sex-linked Genetic Disorders

There are some genetic disorders that you're more likely to end up with if you're male — and it's all thanks to your X and Y chromosomes. Who'd have thought the little blighters could cause so much trouble...

Some Genetic Characteristics Are Sex-linked

1) A characteristic is sex-linked if the allele that codes for it is located on a sex chromosome (X or Y).

2) The Y chromosome is smaller than the X chromosome and carries fewer genes. So most genes on the sex chromosomes are only carried on the X chromosome.

X chromosome

Gene that men only have one allele for.

Gene that men have two alleles for.

Y chromosome

3) As men only have one X chromosome they often only have one allele for sex-linked genes.

4) Because men only have one allele, the characteristic of this allele is shown even if it is recessive. This makes men more likely than women to show recessive characteristics for genes that are sex-linked.

5) Disorders caused by faulty alleles located on sex chromosomes are called sex-linked genetic disorders.

6) Colour blindness and haemophilia (a disease where the sufferer's blood won't clot properly when they cut themselves) are examples of sex-linked genetic disorders.

A Genetic Diagram Shows How Colour Blindness is Inherited

1) Colour blindness is caused by a faulty allele carried on the X chromosome.

2) As it's sex-linked both the chromosome and the allele are written in the genetic diagram, e.g. X^n, where X represents the X chromosome and n the faulty allele for colour vision. The Y chromosome doesn't have an allele for colour vision so is just represented by Y.

3) Women need two copies of the recessive allele to be colour blind, while men only need one copy. This means colour blindness is much rarer in women than men.

4) A woman with only one copy of the recessive allele is a carrier of colour blindness. This means that she isn't colour blind herself, but she can pass the allele on to her offspring.

5) Here's a genetic cross between a carrier female and a normal (non-colour blind) male:

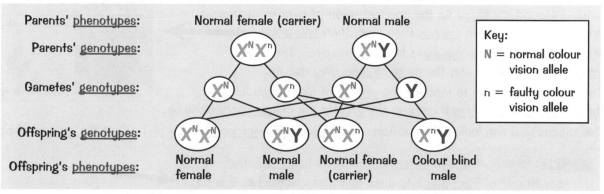

Parents' phenotypes: Normal female (carrier)   Normal male

Parents' genotypes: $X^N X^n$ $X^N Y$

Gametes' genotypes: X^N X^n X^N Y

Offspring's genotypes: $X^N X^N$ $X^N Y$ $X^N X^n$ $X^n Y$

Offspring's phenotypes: Normal female   Normal male   Normal female (carrier)   Colour blind male

Key:
N = normal colour vision allele
n = faulty colour vision allele

6) In the example above, the ratio of normal:colour blind offspring is 3:1. Be careful with this one — it may be disguised as a 2:1:1 ratio (normal:carrier:colour blind), but it means the same thing.

7) In other words, there's a 1 in 4 (25%) chance of a child being colour blind. This rises to 1 in 2 (50%) if you know that the child will be a boy.

Haemophilia is also caused by a faulty allele carried on the X chromosome — it's inherited in the same way as colour blindness. So a genetic diagram for the inheritance of haemophilia will look just the same.

I keep tripping up around the house — I've got a socks-linked disorder...

You know what I said on the last page about drawing the diagram out for yourself and making sure you can follow the working through... Well, I'm going to say it again. Draw the diagram out for yourself and make sure you can follow the working through. There. It mightn't be the most fun drawing ever, but you'll remember how to do it.

Growth of Bacteria

Bacteria are tiny. Really really tiny. But <u>despite their small size</u>, they can have a <u>mighty effect</u> on humans...

Bacteria Reproduce Really, Really Fast

Bacteria reproduce by <u>splitting in two</u>, so the number of bacteria <u>doubles</u> at <u>regular intervals</u>. This means their growth is <u>exponential</u> — to start with, there's only a <u>handful</u> of bacteria but soon there are <u>millions</u> of them. So if a nasty bacterium gets into the body, an <u>infection</u> can develop <u>really fast</u> — <u>before</u> your immune system has a chance to <u>respond</u>.

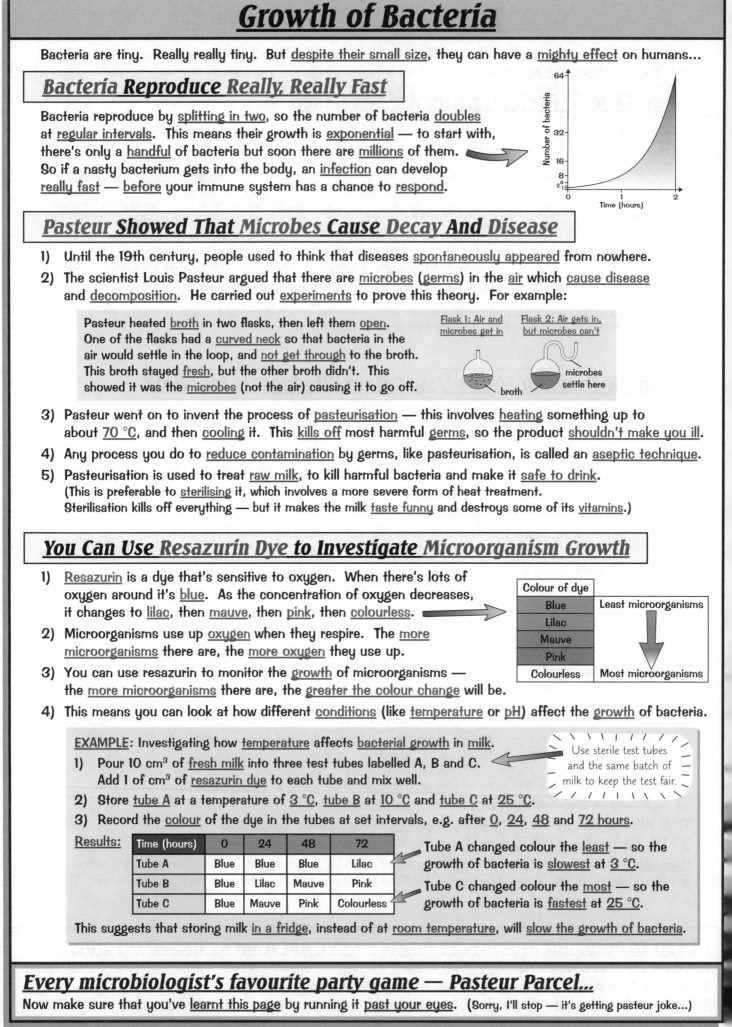

Pasteur Showed That Microbes Cause Decay And Disease

1) Until the 19th century, people used to think that diseases <u>spontaneously appeared</u> from nowhere.

2) The scientist Louis Pasteur argued that there are <u>microbes</u> (<u>germs</u>) in the <u>air</u> which <u>cause disease</u> and <u>decomposition</u>. He carried out <u>experiments</u> to prove this theory. For example:

> Pasteur heated <u>broth</u> in two flasks, then left them <u>open</u>. One of the flasks had a <u>curved neck</u> so that bacteria in the air would settle in the loop, and <u>not get through</u> to the broth. This broth stayed <u>fresh</u>, but the other broth didn't. This showed it was the <u>microbes</u> (not the air) causing it to go off.
>
> **Flask 1: Air and microbes get in** **Flask 2: Air gets in, but microbes can't**
>
> broth   microbes settle here

3) Pasteur went on to invent the process of <u>pasteurisation</u> — this involves <u>heating</u> something up to about <u>70 °C</u>, and then <u>cooling</u> it. This <u>kills off</u> most harmful <u>germs</u>, so the product <u>shouldn't make you ill</u>.

4) Any process you do to <u>reduce contamination</u> by germs, like pasteurisation, is called an <u>aseptic technique</u>.

5) Pasteurisation is used to treat <u>raw milk</u>, to kill harmful bacteria and make it <u>safe to drink</u>. (This is preferable to <u>sterilising</u> it, which involves a more severe form of heat treatment. Sterilisation kills off everything — but it makes the milk <u>taste funny</u> and destroys some of its <u>vitamins</u>.)

You Can Use Resazurin Dye to Investigate Microorganism Growth

1) <u>Resazurin</u> is a dye that's sensitive to oxygen. When there's lots of oxygen around it's <u>blue</u>. As the concentration of oxygen decreases, it changes to <u>lilac</u>, then <u>mauve</u>, then <u>pink</u>, then <u>colourless</u>.

2) Microorganisms use up <u>oxygen</u> when they respire. The <u>more microorganisms</u> there are, the <u>more oxygen</u> they use up.

3) You can use resazurin to monitor the <u>growth</u> of microorganisms — the <u>more microorganisms</u> there are, the <u>greater the colour change</u> will be.

Colour of dye	
Blue	Least microorganisms
Lilac	
Mauve	
Pink	
Colourless	Most microorganisms

4) This means you can look at how different <u>conditions</u> (like <u>temperature</u> or <u>pH</u>) affect the <u>growth</u> of bacteria.

> <u>EXAMPLE</u>: Investigating how <u>temperature</u> affects <u>bacterial growth</u> in <u>milk</u>.
>
> 1) Pour 10 cm³ of <u>fresh milk</u> into three test tubes labelled A, B and C. Add 1 of cm³ of <u>resazurin dye</u> to each tube and mix well.
>
> *Use sterile test tubes and the same batch of milk to keep the test fair.*
>
> 2) Store <u>tube A</u> at a temperature of <u>3 °C</u>, <u>tube B</u> at <u>10 °C</u> and <u>tube C</u> at <u>25 °C</u>.
>
> 3) Record the <u>colour</u> of the dye in the tubes at set intervals, e.g. after <u>0</u>, <u>24</u>, <u>48</u> and <u>72 hours</u>.
>
> Results:
>
> | Time (hours) | 0 | 24 | 48 | 72 |
> |---|---|---|---|---|
> | Tube A | Blue | Blue | Blue | Lilac |
> | Tube B | Blue | Lilac | Mauve | Pink |
> | Tube C | Blue | Mauve | Pink | Colourless |
>
> Tube A changed colour the <u>least</u> — so the growth of bacteria is <u>slowest</u> at <u>3 °C</u>.
>
> Tube C changed colour the <u>most</u> — so the growth of bacteria is <u>fastest</u> at <u>25 °C</u>.
>
> This suggests that storing milk <u>in a fridge</u>, instead of at <u>room temperature</u>, will <u>slow the growth of bacteria</u>.

Every microbiologist's favourite party game — Pasteur Parcel...

Now make sure that you've <u>learnt this page</u> by running it <u>past your eyes</u>. (Sorry, I'll stop — it's getting pasteur joke...)

The Immune System

If only your body had some way of stopping infections developing... why hang on a sec, it blummin' well does.

Your Immune System Deals with Infectious Microorganisms

1) Once microorganisms have entered your body they'll <u>reproduce rapidly</u> unless they're destroyed.

2) That's the job of your <u>immune system</u>, and <u>white blood cells</u> are the most important part of it.

3) White blood cells travel around in your <u>blood</u> and crawl into every part of you, <u>patrolling</u> for microorganisms.

4) Some of the <u>white blood cells</u> that you have in your body are a special type called <u>B-lymphocytes</u>. When B-lymphocytes come across an <u>invading microorganism</u> they respond by producing <u>antibodies</u>:

> 1) Every pathogen has <u>unique molecules</u> on the <u>surface</u> of its cells — no two species have the same ones. These molecules are called <u>antigens</u>.
>
> 2) When your B-lymphocytes come across a <u>foreign antigen</u> (like those on the surface of a bacterium) they start to produce proteins called <u>antibodies</u>, which bind (lock on) to and kill the new invading cells. The antibodies produced are <u>specific</u> to that pathogen — they won't lock on to other pathogens.
>
> 3) Antibodies are then produced rapidly and flow all round the body to kill all <u>similar</u> bacteria or viruses.

Memory Lymphocytes Give Immunity To Later Infection

1) When a <u>pathogen</u> enters the body for the <u>first time</u> the response is <u>slow</u> because there <u>aren't many B-lymphocytes</u> that can make the antibody needed to lock on to the antigen.

2) Eventually the body will produce <u>enough</u> of the right antibody to overcome the infection. Meanwhile the infected person will show <u>symptoms</u> of the disease.

3) After being exposed to an antigen, a special type of B-lymphocyte is produced called a <u>memory lymphocyte</u>. Memory lymphocytes <u>remain in the body</u> for a <u>long time</u>, and 'remember' a specific antibody.

4) The person is now <u>immune</u> — their immune system has the <u>ability</u> to respond <u>quickly</u> to a second infection.

5) If the <u>same pathogen</u> enters the body again, the immune system will produce a <u>quicker</u>, <u>stronger</u> immune response.

6) The secondary response often gets rid of the pathogen <u>before</u> you begin to show any <u>symptoms</u>.

7) This can all be shown in a lovely <u>graph</u>:

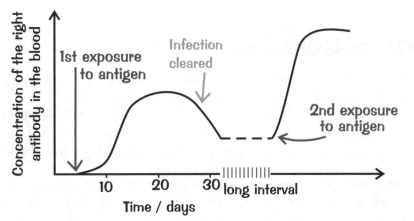

Take that, you evil antigen...

Today's learning recommendation: get someone at home to lurk behind the furniture and jump out at you, shouting "antigen" or "antibody". Quick as a flash, you must give the <u>right definition</u>. Once your memory's as good as a memory lymphocyte's, you can reward yourself with some immunisation stuff on the next page. Ooooo, enjoy.

Immunisation

An ounce of prevention is worth a pound of cure. That's what my mum says, anyhow.

Immunisation Stops You Getting Infections

1) To avoid getting ill you can be immunised against some diseases, e.g. measles.

2) Immunisation involves injecting dead or inactive microorganisms into the body. These are antigenic (they carry antigens), so even though they're harmless your body makes antibodies to attack them.

3) The antigens also trigger memory lymphocytes to be made.

4) If live micro-organisms of the same type appear after that, they'll be killed immediately by the antibodies which you've already developed against them. Cool.

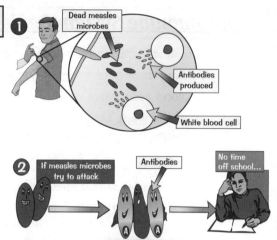

Jenner Used Cowpox To Safely Immunise Against Smallpox

Edward Jenner invented the first vaccine. It worked against a disease called smallpox.

1) Smallpox killed lots of people in the 1700s, and left horrible scars on people that survived it.

2) Edward Jenner knew that people who had cowpox (a mild disease caught from cattle) didn't catch smallpox.

3) In 1796 he took bits of scab from a girl with cowpox...

...and put them into a cut on the arm of a boy.

The boy was a bit unwell, but then recovered.

Then Jenner exposed the boy to smallpox.

The boy didn't catch smallpox.

4) The cowpox antigens triggered the boy's B-lymphocytes to produce antibodies. Because smallpox has some of the same antigens as cowpox, when the boy was infected with smallpox his immune system quickly produced antibodies to stop him from getting the disease.

There are Pros and Cons of Immunisation

PROS

1) Big outbreaks of diseases, called epidemics, can be prevented if a large percentage of the population are immunised. Even the people who aren't immunised are unlikely to catch the disease because there are fewer people able to pass it on. But if a significant number of people aren't immunised, the disease can spread quickly through them and lots of people will be ill at the same time.

2) Some diseases, e.g. smallpox, have been virtually wiped out by immunisation programmes.

CONS

1) Immunisation doesn't always work — sometimes it doesn't give you immunity.

2) You can sometimes have a bad reaction to a vaccine (e.g. swelling, or maybe something more serious like a fever or seizures). But bad reactions are very rare.

Medicine 1700s style — try putting someone else's scab on it...

So, we should all thank James Phipps, the lad that Jenner did his first experiment on, as well as the 23 people he then treated. By proving they were immune to smallpox, Jenner invented a procedure that's saved millions of lives.

Monoclonal Antibodies

Antibodies aren't only used by the immune system — they can also used to see if a woman is <u>pregnant</u> or not.

Monoclonal Antibodies *are Identical* Antibodies

1) Antibodies are produced by <u>B-lymphocytes</u> (see p.79).

2) If you found a <u>really useful antibody</u> you'd probably want to make <u>lots of identical copies</u> of it. So you might try to grab the B-lymphocyte that made the antibody and grow more of them. Unfortunately though, B-lymphocytes <u>don't divide very easily</u>.

3) <u>Tumour cells</u>, on the other hand, don't produce antibodies but <u>divide lots</u> — so they can be <u>grown really easily</u>.

4) It's possible to <u>fuse</u> a <u>B-lymphocyte</u> with a <u>tumour cell</u> to create a cell called a <u>hybridoma</u>. Hybridoma cells <u>divide</u> really <u>quickly</u> to produce <u>lots</u> of <u>identical antibodies</u>, called <u>monoclonal antibodies</u>.

5) You can make monoclonal antibodies that <u>bind to anything</u> you want, e.g. an antigen that's only found on the surface of <u>one type of cell</u>. Monoclonal antibodies are really useful because they will <u>only</u> bind to (target) <u>this molecule</u>.

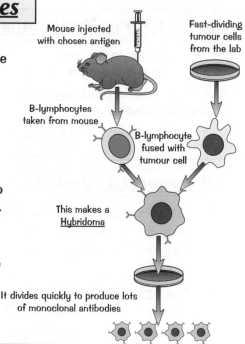

Mouse injected with chosen antigen

Fast-dividing tumour cells from the lab

B-lymphocytes taken from mouse

B-lymphocyte fused with tumour cell

This makes a <u>Hybridoma</u>

It divides quickly to produce lots of monoclonal antibodies

Monoclonal Antibodies *Are Used In Pregnancy Tests*

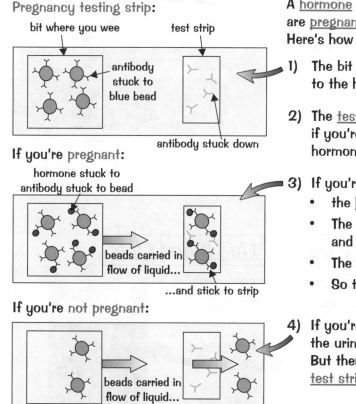

Pregnancy testing strip:

bit where you wee

test strip

antibody stuck to blue bead

antibody stuck down

If you're pregnant:

hormone stuck to antibody stuck to bead

beads carried in flow of liquid...

...and stick to strip

If you're not pregnant:

beads carried in flow of liquid...

...but don't stick

A <u>hormone</u> is found in the <u>urine</u> of women <u>only</u> when they are <u>pregnant</u>. <u>Pregnancy testing sticks</u> detect this hormone. Here's how they work:

1) The bit of the stick you <u>wee on</u> has some <u>antibodies</u> to the hormone, with <u>blue beads attached</u>.

2) The <u>test strip</u> (the bit of the stick that turns blue if you're pregnant) has some more antibodies to the hormone <u>stuck onto it</u> (so that they can't move).

3) If you're <u>pregnant</u> and you wee on the stick:
   - the <u>hormone binds</u> to the <u>antibodies</u> on the <u>blue beads</u>.
   - The urine <u>moves up</u> the stick, <u>carrying</u> the hormone and the beads.
   - The beads and hormone <u>bind</u> to the antibodies on the strip.
   - So the <u>blue beads</u> get <u>stuck on the strip</u>, turning it <u>blue</u>.

4) If you're <u>not pregnant</u> and you wee on the stick, the urine <u>still</u> moves up the stick, carrying the <u>blue beads</u>. But there's <u>nothing</u> to <u>stick</u> the blue beads onto the <u>test strip</u>, so it <u>doesn't go blue</u>.

Hybridomas — sound like monsters out of Dr Who to me...

Pregnancy testing sticks are a really clever invention — they mean that a woman can find out <u>for sure</u> if she's pregnant or not <u>fairly quickly</u>. You need to know <u>how they work</u> — from the <u>hormones</u> to the <u>monoclonal antibodies</u> to the <u>blue beads</u>. Who'd have thought there was so much clever technology behind weeing on a stick...

More on Monoclonal Antibodies

It's possible to <u>attach drugs</u> to <u>monoclonal antibodies</u>. You can think of them as very very tiny yet very very angry homing pigeons, which'll go after one specific kind of <u>target</u> and, er, peck it to bits.

You Can Make Monoclonal Antibodies That Stick to Cancer Cells

1) <u>Different cells</u> in the body have <u>different antigens</u> on their cell <u>surface</u>. So you can make monoclonal antibodies that will bind to <u>specific cells</u> in the body (e.g. just liver cells).

2) Cancer cells have <u>antigens</u> on their <u>cell membranes</u> that <u>aren't</u> found on normal body cells. They're called <u>tumour markers</u>.

3) In the lab, you can make <u>monoclonal antibodies</u> that will <u>bind</u> to these tumour markers. They can be used to help <u>diagnose</u> and <u>treat</u> cancer.

Monoclonal Antibodies Can Be Used To Diagnose Cancer...

1) First, the <u>antibodies</u> are <u>labelled</u> with a radioactive element.

2) Then, the <u>labelled antibodies</u> are given to a patient through a <u>drip</u>. They go into the <u>blood</u> are carried around the body.

3) When the antibodies come into <u>contact</u> with the cancer cells they <u>bind</u> to the tumour markers.

4) A <u>picture</u> of the patient's body is taken using a special <u>camera</u> that detects <u>radioactivity</u>. Anywhere there are <u>cancer cells</u> will show up as a <u>bright spot</u>.

5) Doctors can see exactly <u>where</u> the cancer is, <u>what size</u> it is, and find out if it is <u>spreading</u>.

...and to Target Drugs to Cancer Cells

1) An <u>anti-cancer drug</u> is attached to monoclonal antibodies.

2) The antibodies are <u>given</u> to the patient through a drip.

3) The antibodies <u>target specific cells</u> (the cancer cells) because they only bind to the <u>tumour markers</u>.

4) The drug <u>kills</u> the <u>cancer cells</u> but <u>doesn't</u> kill any <u>normal body cells</u> near the tumour.

5) Other cancer treatments (like other <u>drugs</u> and <u>radiotherapy</u>) <u>can</u> affect normal body cells <u>as well as</u> killing cancer cells.

6) So the <u>side effects</u> of an antibody-based drug are <u>lower</u> than for other drugs or radiotherapy.

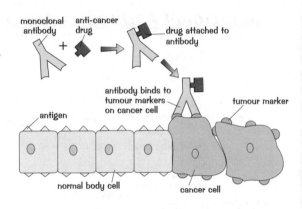

monoclonal antibody   anti-cancer drug   drug attached to antibody

antibody binds to tumour markers on cancer cell

tumour marker

antigen

normal body cell   cancer cell

Radiotherapy involves firing high-energy beams (like X-rays) straight at a tumour.

Monoclonal Antibodies Can Also Be Used To Find Blood Clots

1) When blood <u>clots</u>, <u>proteins</u> in the blood <u>join together</u> to form a solid mesh.

2) <u>Monoclonal antibodies</u> have been developed that <u>bind</u> to these <u>proteins</u>.

3) You can <u>attach</u> a <u>radioactive element</u> to these antibodies.

4) Then, if you inject them into the body and take a picture using a <u>camera</u> that picks up the <u>radiation</u>, that picture will have a really <u>bright spot</u> where a there is a blood clot.

5) This is useful because you can <u>easily find</u> a potentially harmful <u>blood clot</u> (and get rid of it before it harms the patient).

Bonoclonal antibodies — can be used to stick hats onto popular singers...

<u>Monoclonal antibodies</u> are really useful for <u>finding stuff</u>. Imagine having a horde of trained fireflies to search for your lost keys, or phone, or remote control. Instead of you having to search under everything, you just <u>release</u> the fireflies and wait for them to <u>cluster</u> around your lost stuff, in a big obvious glowing mass. <u>Genius</u>.

Drugs From Plants and Plant Diseases

We're constantly developing <u>new drugs</u> (like new <u>antibiotics</u>) to deal with things that we <u>couldn't treat</u> before.

Many Drugs Come from Plants

1) <u>Plants</u> produce a variety of <u>chemicals</u> to <u>defend</u> themselves against <u>pests</u> (e.g. caterpillars) and <u>pathogens</u>.

2) Some of these chemicals can be used as <u>drugs</u> to <u>treat</u> human diseases or <u>relieve symptoms</u>.
   A lot of our <u>current medicines</u> were discovered by studying plants used in <u>traditional cures</u>.

3) Here are some <u>examples</u> of drugs you might come across...

1) Aspirin

• <u>Aspirin</u> is used to treat many types of <u>pain</u>, and to lower <u>fever</u>.

• Aspirin was developed from a chemical found in the leaves and bark of the <u>willow tree</u>.

2) Taxol®

• Taxol® is an <u>anti-cancer</u> drug.

• It comes from the bark of the <u>Pacific yew tree</u>.

• It was discovered when scientists were <u>screening</u> (testing) loads of plants, looking for <u>potential treatments</u>.

These are just examples — you don't have to learn them all, as long as you know at least one.

3) Quinine

• <u>Quinine</u> comes from a South American <u>cinchona tree</u>.

• For years, it was the main treatment against <u>malaria</u> (an infectious disease carried by mosquitoes).

Pests Can Massively Reduce Crop Yields

1) A lot of crops are <u>lost</u> each year because of <u>pests</u> such as <u>insects</u> (e.g. fruit flies), <u>weeds</u> (e.g. dandelions) and <u>pathogens</u> (e.g. fungi).

2) Different pests reduce crop yields in different ways, for example:

   • <u>Fruit flies</u> feed on, erm, fruit so they can <u>ruin entire fruit crops</u>.

   • <u>Weeds</u> that grow near plants compete for the <u>nutrients</u> in the soil. If the plant gets fewer nutrients, it won't grow as well and the crop <u>yield</u> (the <u>amount of food</u> a crop produces) will be <u>lower</u>.

   • If a plant is infected with a <u>pathogen</u>, some of its <u>energy</u> is <u>taken</u> by the pathogen (e.g. fungi take nutrients from host plants) or used to <u>replace bits</u> that have been killed. This means less energy is used to make <u>useful things</u> like apples, wheat or carrots, so the <u>yield</u> is <u>lower</u>. <u>Heavy infestation</u> by a pathogen can mean a <u>whole field</u> of plants produces <u>no food at all</u>.

3) Pests also add to the <u>cost</u> of <u>producing food</u>, as money must be spent on <u>pesticides</u> (e.g. fungicides to get rid of fungal diseases) and <u>disease-resistant</u> or <u>insect-resistant</u> crops.

4) Low crop yields can <u>drive up</u> the <u>price</u> of food for <u>consumers</u>.

My garden looks really poorly — It's got terrible treesles...

It's not just people that <u>get ill</u> — <u>plants</u> catch some pretty nasty <u>diseases</u> too. I certainly wouldn't want to have toadstools growing out of my branches, that's for sure. Luckily for us, lots of the <u>chemicals</u> that plants produce to <u>interfere</u> with the bacteria and fungi crawling all over them, can also be used as <u>drugs</u> for us. Yippee.

Daily Rhythms

Plants and animals use <u>time</u> in lots of ways that you might not expect. Many plants can <u>keep track</u> of how <u>long</u> the <u>day</u> is. And lots of plants and animals also have an <u>internal clock</u> that tells them the <u>time of day</u>.

Plants Are Photoperiodic — They Respond To Changes In Day Length

1) In the summer, <u>days</u> are <u>long</u> and <u>nights</u> are <u>short</u>. The <u>day length</u> gradually <u>increases</u> from <u>midwinter</u> to <u>midsummer</u> (June 20-21 in the northern hemisphere), and then gradually <u>decreases</u> again.

2) A <u>photoperiodic response</u> is a response to a change in the <u>amount of light and dark</u> in a 24 hour cycle. Some plants only <u>germinate</u> (sprout from seeds), <u>grow</u> or <u>flower</u> given a certain <u>amount of light and dark</u>. These responses make sure they <u>grow</u> or <u>reproduce</u> at the <u>time of year</u> that best suits them. For example:

> <u>Seeds</u> of some <u>Arctic plants</u> only <u>germinate</u> if the <u>days</u> are <u>very long</u>. This makes sure they only germinate in the <u>middle of summer</u>, when <u>temperatures</u> are <u>warm</u>.

> Some plant <u>buds</u> use the <u>increasing day length</u> to tell them that it's <u>far</u> enough away from <u>winter</u> to start to <u>grow</u>. This makes sure they don't <u>sprout</u> only to be <u>killed</u> by <u>frost</u>.

> • Some plants (long-day plants, e.g. spinach) only <u>flower</u> when the <u>day</u> is <u>at least</u> a certain length — to make sure they flower <u>near to midsummer</u>.
> • Other plants (short day plants, e.g. primroses) only <u>flower</u> when the <u>days</u> are <u>less than</u> a certain length — to make sure they flower in the <u>early spring</u> or <u>autumn</u>.
> • This way, they only flower when the right <u>insects</u> are about to <u>pollinate</u> the flowers.

Circadian Rhythms are Daily Cycles in Living Things

1) <u>Circadian rhythms</u> are biological processes that follow a <u>24 hour cycle</u>.

2) They include <u>chemical patterns</u> (e.g. hormone production), <u>physiological patterns</u> (e.g. body temperature) and <u>patterns of behaviour</u> (e.g. sleeping and eating).

3) <u>Animals</u>, <u>plants</u> and <u>microorganisms</u> all have circadian rhythms.

4) Circadian rhythms are <u>controlled internally</u>, but they can be <u>influenced</u> by <u>environmental factors</u> (like light intensity).

> The 'master clock' is a group of nerve cells in the brain.

5) Examples of circadian rhythms in <u>animals</u> include:

> <u>Sleep patterns</u>: The body's <u>master clock</u> gets information about <u>light intensity</u> from your <u>eyes</u>. It uses this to control production of the hormone <u>melatonin</u>, which makes you sleepy.
> • When it gets <u>dark</u>, your melatonin production <u>increases</u>. (The opposite happens in <u>nocturnal animals</u>.)
> • Having <u>regular sleep patterns</u> is good for your <u>health</u> and helps you to feel <u>awake</u> at the right times.

> <u>Urine production</u>: The body's <u>master clock</u> also controls production of <u>ADH</u> (see page 72). At <u>night</u> ADH levels <u>increase</u>. This reduces <u>urine production</u> (so your sleep isn't interrupted).

6) Examples of circadian rhythms in <u>plants</u> include:

> <u>Stomata opening</u>: <u>Stomata</u> respond to <u>light intensity</u> — they <u>open</u> during the <u>day</u> and <u>close</u> at <u>night</u>.
> • During the day <u>photosynthesis</u> occurs. The stomata open to let CO_2 and O_2 in and out.
> • At night photosynthesis <u>stops</u>, so the stomata can <u>close</u> to <u>reduce water loss</u>.

> <u>Flower opening</u>: Plants can respond to <u>light intensity</u> by opening and closing their <u>flowers</u> at different times of day. They only need to be open when the creatures that <u>pollinate</u> them are <u>active</u> — e.g. <u>tobacco flowers</u>, which are pollinated by <u>moths</u>, only open at <u>night</u>.

So that's why I keep falling asleep in my sunglasses...

<u>Jet lag</u> is a classic example of what happens if you monkey around with your <u>daily rhythms</u>. If you stay up in the <u>light</u> when your brain thinks it should be <u>night</u>, your body clock can't work out what's going on. You won't be able to get to sleep, you'll get tired and groggy and (probably) start spouting rubbish. Potato. Hedgehog. Robots. Zzzzzzzₐₐ....

Revision Summary for B3 Topic 1

It's the end of the section. And that can only mean one thing. Yep... it's time for a good ol' revision summary. That's right — it's time to see how much you've learned in this section. Which had better be everything, frankly — or you're going to have to go back and learn the stuff again — properly, this time. So heads down, eyes open — and get ready to see how much revision you need, or don't need, to do...

1)   State the three main roles of the kidneys.
2)   Name two things that are reabsorbed by kidneys.
3)   What is osmoregulation?
4)   How does a dialysis machine work? Which substances does it remove from the blood?
5)   What are the advantages and disadvantages of a kidney transplant over dialysis?
6)   Describe two ways that sperm cells are specialised for their role in reproduction.
7)   Briefly describe what happens in each of the four stages of the menstrual cycle.
8)   Which four hormones control the menstrual cycle? What exactly do they do?
9)   Give one example of how the menstrual cycle is controlled by negative feedback.
10) Describe one type of fertility treatment. Give one pro and one con of this fertility treatment.
11) Which chromosome in the human body causes male characteristics?
12) Copy and complete the diagrams below to show what happens to the X and Y chromosomes during reproduction.

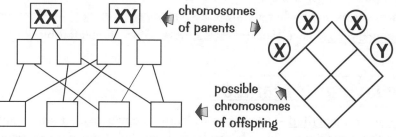

13)* A couple have three boys already. What is the probability that their fourth child will be a girl? (Hint: this may be a nasty trick question — don't be fooled.)
14) What is a sex-linked genetic disorder? Give an example of such a disorder.
15) Describe Louis Pasteur's experiment with flasks of broth. What did it show?
16) Describe an experiment you could do using resazurin dye to investigate how temperature affects the growth of bacteria.
17) Explain how memory lymphocytes stop you getting ill if you're exposed to a pathogen for a second time.
18) Explain how immunisation stops you getting infections.
19) Describe Edward Jenner's experiment with cowpox.
20) Describe the pros and cons of immunisation.
21) What are monoclonal antibodies?
22) Explain how a pregnancy testing stick works.
23) Describe how monoclonal antibodies can be used to treat cancer.
24) Why is using monoclonal antibodies to treat cancer better than using other drugs or radiotherapy?
25) Name one chemical, produced by plants, that humans use as a drug to treat disease.
26) What is a photoperiodic response? Give one example a photoperiodic response in a plant.
27) Give one example of a circadian rhythm in: a) an animal, b) a plant.

*Answer to this question is on p.108.

Innate and Learned Behaviour

Behaviour is a pretty complicated topic, but pretty interesting too...

Behaviour is an Organism's Response to Changes in Its Environment

1) Behaviour is how an organism responds to things going on in its environment — helping it to survive.

2) Behaviour can either be inherited or learned, but most behaviour relies on a combination of the two.

3) Both your genes and your environment play a part in influencing your behaviour and it's sometimes hard to decide what is inherited and what is learned.

Some Behaviour is Innate...

Inherited behaviour is known as innate behaviour. Animals can respond in the right way to a stimulus straight away, even though they've never done it before, e.g. newborn mammals have an instinct to suckle from their mothers. Innate behaviour can be a simple reflex, or a complicated behaviour, like a courtship ritual.

Reflex actions are simple inherited behaviours, where a stimulus produces a fairly simple response, like sneezing, salivation, and blinking. They often protect us from dangerous stimuli. Reflexes are automatic — you don't have to think about them.

A stimulus is a detectable change in the environment.

Some types of reflex are slightly more complex:

1) Earthworms show what's known as 'negative phototaxis' — they move away from light.

2) Sea anemones wave their tentacles more when stimulated by chemicals emitted by their prey.

...Some Behaviour is Learned...

Learned behaviour isn't inherited — you have to learn it, obviously. It lets animals respond to changing conditions. Animals can learn from their previous experiences how to avoid predators and harmful food, and how to find food or a suitable mate.

HABITUATION If you keep on giving an animal a stimulus that isn't beneficial or harmful to it, it quickly learns not to respond to it. This is called habituation. This is why crows eventually learn to ignore scarecrows (because they don't harm the bird or reward it).

By ignoring non-threatening and non-rewarding stimuli, animals can spend their time and energy more efficiently. This is an especially important learning process in young animals — they are born with an inherited tendency to be frightened by loud, bright, sudden stimuli and they must quickly learn which stimuli to ignore so they can concentrate on stimuli that are possibly dangerous.

...and Some Behaviour is a Mixture of the Two

1) Imprinting is when an animal learns to recognise its parents, and instinctively follows them. So it's is a combination of a learned behaviour and an innate behaviour

2) Imprinting occurs in species which can move soon after they're born. A newborn animal has an instinct to follow the first moving object it sees — usually a parent, who provides shelter and food (helping it survive).

3) But the animal has no innate instinct of what its parents look like — they have to learn this.

There's more about imprinting on p.89

Ducklings usually imprint on their parents. But if they are reared from birth by a human, the human is the first moving object the ducklings see so they imprint on the human (and follow them).

I think I have negative revisiontaxis...

Habituation happens more often than you think — e.g. you learn to ignore the stimuli produced by the weight of your clothes because you're used to wearing them. There is also a type of habituation nicknamed 'banner blindness' where internet users fail to notice advertising banners after a while.

Conditioning

Habituation isn't the only type of learned behaviour — there are more...

Conditioning is Another Form of Learned Behaviour

There are two types of conditioning:

Classical Conditioning

Classical conditioning happens when an animal learns PASSIVELY (i.e. without actually trying) to associate a 'neutral stimulus' with an important one, e.g. a dog associates a bell ringing with the arrival of food. The response is automatic and reinforced by repetition.

Example: Ivan Pavlov — Classical Conditioning in Dogs
Pavlov studied the behaviour of dogs and noticed that they would salivate (drool) every time they saw or smelt food. He began to ring a bell just before each time the dogs were given their food. After a while he found that the dogs salivated when the bell was rung even if he didn't give them their food.

Operant Conditioning

Operant conditioning or 'trial and error learning' is where an animal learns ACTIVELY to associate an action with a reward or a punishment. (So the animal actually tries to work out what's going on.) This happens in humans when children are rewarded or punished for specific behaviour.

Example: Burrhus Skinner — Operant Behaviour in Pigeons and Rats
Skinner trained rats and pigeons to obtain a food reward using a small cage that he invented (called a 'Skinner box'). The animal had a choice of buttons to press. When the animal pressed a particular lever or button, it was rewarded with food. He found that pigeons and rats used a system of trial and error to learn which button to press to get the reward.

We Use Conditioning to Train Animals

Humans use both classical and operant conditioning to train animals to do certain things.

Training animals usually involves operant conditioning — giving rewards when the animal does what you want or punishments when it does something you don't want it to do. Rewards like food treats work best, but sometimes just praise will do. Punishments can be physical (like choke chains which pull around a dog's neck if it pulls on the lead) or verbal (like saying 'No!'). However, punishment isn't recommended any more for animal training — it's stressful for the animal and rewards work just as well.

Here are some examples of animal training using operant conditioning:

* Training guide dogs to stop at a roadside and wait for a command.
* Training police sniffer dogs to retrieve drugs.
* Training police horses to only respond to commands from their riders.

Classical conditioning is used in combination with operant conditioning when the reward can't be given at the exact time the act is carried out. For example, a dolphin can't always be rewarded with fish at the exact moment it does a jump. The trainer gets the dolphin to learn to associate a whistle with getting fish, then whistles when the animal does the jump. The whistle is, in a way, the reward, as it tells the dolphin that it will get a fish.

I condition my hair to make it lie down...

Here's how to condition your teacher. If your teacher is one of those active types that like to stroll backwards and forwards while talking to you, simply look interested while they're on one side of room, and bored while they're on the other. In no time, they'll only be teaching from one side of the room.

Social Behaviour and Communication

You thought it was only humans that had social lives and nice chats? Wrong!

Animals Need to Communicate

Communication between different individuals in a group is beneficial in a number of ways:

1) It can help keep the group together.
2) If any one animal sees a predator, it can warn all the others.
3) Communication of mood can avoid unnecessary fighting.
4) Baby animals can communicate their needs to their parents.
5) Communication can allow predators hunting in a pack to coordinate their attack.

Animals Can Communicate in Different Ways

SOUND

Communication by sound is pretty common in nature, and occurs in humans too — through language.

- Whales and dolphins can communicate over long distances using low-frequency sound.
- Birds' calls are used to declare their territory, attract a mate or warn others about predators.

CHEMICALS

Chemicals called pheromones can be released by an animal to tell others where it is or where it has been:

- Many animals use chemical 'scents' to mark the boundaries of their territory, e.g. dogs pee on things.
- Other chemicals can act as sexual attractants. In some moths, the male can detect the female's pheromone even if he's several kilometres away from her.

VISUAL SIGNALS

Some animals use specific visual signals to communicate:

- Honey bees move in a certain way, called a 'waggle dance', when they return to the hive to tell others where they've found food.
- Most mammals can communicate certain intentions through their body posture (how they hold themselves) and gestures (small movements).
- For example, many use behaviours to threaten others — to intimidate them and so avoid an actual fight. Chimps do this by staring or raising an arm.
- Just as behaviours are used to threaten, they're also used to admit defeat — for example, a dog rolling on its back is showing submission. There are plenty of courtship behaviours in different species too — from funny dances to offering gifts to building elaborate nests.
- Another sort of visual communication signal is facial expressions. We're all familiar with human expressions, but we shouldn't apply them to other animals, because facial expressions can mean different things in different species.

Male peacocks raise and shake their fancy tail feathers as a courtship display.

To us, this chimp looks like he's laughing, but really he's showing fear.

Bad dancing — not very attractive to a female of any species...

Spare a thought for all the chimps you've ever seen in TV ads. They'll be dressed up in human clothes, pouring each other tea, and apparently sharing a joke. But in order to make their 'laughter' facial expression, they weren't tickled or told something funny — they were probably frightened. Poor guys.

Animal Behaviour Studies

A <u>scientist</u> who <u>studies</u> the <u>behaviour of animals</u> is called an <u>ethologist</u>. Save that one for when you're on QI.

Ethologists Study Animal Behaviour

Here are <u>studies</u> by <u>four ethologists</u> that you need to know about:

Tinbergen: Studied Innate Behaviour in Gulls

1) <u>Nikolaas Tinbergen</u> studied <u>innate behaviour</u> (see p.86) in <u>herring gulls</u>.

2) Newly hatched <u>gull chicks</u> know how to <u>peck</u> at their <u>parent's beak</u> to ask for <u>food</u>. <u>Adult gulls</u> have a <u>red spot</u> on their beak. Tinbergen wanted to find out if it was this red spot that made the chicks want to peck the beak and get food.

3) He showed newly hatched chicks <u>cardboard</u> gull heads with <u>different colour spots</u> on the beaks. He <u>counted</u> the number of times that the chicks <u>pecked</u> the different spots in a <u>given time</u>.

4) The chicks pecked at the beaks with <u>red spots</u> most often. Tinbergen concluded that the chicks are born with an <u>instinct</u> to <u>peck</u> at the red spot — and that helps them to <u>find food</u>.

Lorenz: Studied Imprinting in Geese

1) In 1935 <u>Konrad Lorenz</u> studied how baby birds, like ducklings and goose chicks, <u>recognise</u> their mother and learn to <u>follow her around</u>.

2) He took <u>two groups</u> of <u>goose eggs</u>. <u>Group 1</u> were hatched out by their own mother, while <u>Group 2</u> were hatched in an <u>incubator</u> (with <u>no mother</u> (Aww...)).

3) The first <u>moving object</u> that the goose chicks in <u>Group 1</u> saw was their <u>mother</u>. For the goose chicks in <u>Group 2</u> it was <u>Lorenz</u>.

4) The goose chicks in <u>Group 2</u> (from the <u>incubator</u>) treated <u>Lorenz</u> the same as the <u>Group 1</u> goose chicks treated their <u>mother</u> — they <u>followed</u> him around.

5) The goose chicks had formed an attachment to the <u>first</u> moving object they <u>saw</u>. This is <u>imprinting</u> (see p.86) and it helps the goose chicks to <u>recognise</u> their mother*.

Fossey and Goodall: Studied Social Behaviour in Apes

> Chimpanzees and gorillas are both apes.

1) <u>Dian Fossey</u> studied <u>mountain gorillas</u> in Africa between 1967 and 1985.

2) <u>Jane Goodall</u> studied <u>chimpanzees</u> in Tanzania between 1960 and 2005.

3) Fossey and Goodall spent time getting close to the apes in their <u>natural habitats</u> so that they didn't disturb them. They <u>watched</u> the animals carefully to see how they <u>behaved</u> and <u>recorded</u> what they saw.

4) Both <u>gorillas</u> and <u>chimpanzees</u> are <u>social</u> animals — they live in <u>groups</u>.

5) <u>Fossey</u> and <u>Goodall</u> saw plenty of examples of the gorillas and chimps using <u>social behaviour</u>:

- The apes <u>worked together</u> to <u>search</u> for <u>food</u> sources — so they found <u>more food</u>.
- They protected each other from <u>attacks</u> (so they were safer than they would be on their own).
- All of the <u>males</u> in the group had a <u>social rank</u> (with the most <u>dominant</u> at the top). This helped to <u>prevent fights</u> (which waste energy) because everyone knew their place in the group.
- The apes <u>groomed</u> each other (picked out insects and dirt from each other's fur). This helped to keep them clean, but also reinforced the <u>social bonds</u> within the group, helping to <u>keep it together</u>. They also strengthened these bonds by showing <u>affection</u> (e.g. by <u>hugging</u> each other).

Wanted: one research ethologist. Must enjoy making cardboard seagulls...

<u>Ethologists</u> are a pretty committed bunch in general. To get close to her gorillas, <u>Dian Fossey</u> had to <u>imitate</u> them so they got used to her. Apparently she <u>grunted</u> at them, <u>groomed</u> them and <u>ate wild celery</u>. Now that's dedication for you. Mind you, at least she didn't spend her days being stalked by confused geese like <u>Konrad Lorenz</u>.

*Assuming that there aren't any interfering ethologists about that is.

Investigating Animal Behaviour

If you want to <u>investigate</u> animal behaviour, you're going to need a simple <u>experiment</u> you can do in the lab. That's where <u>choice chambers</u> come in. Drumroll please...

You Can Use <u>Choice Chambers to Investigate Animal Behaviour</u>

1) A <u>choice chamber</u> is a container that's divided up into two or more <u>chambers</u>.

2) You can set up <u>different environments</u> inside each chamber, like a <u>dark</u> section, or a <u>wet</u> section.

3) Then you pop some <u>animals</u> (usually <u>insects</u>) inside and watch which chamber they <u>move to</u>. <u>Most</u> of them will head to the section with the environmental conditions that are <u>closest</u> to their <u>natural habitat</u>.

4) That means that you can use choice chambers to look at how animals <u>respond</u> to <u>environmental conditions</u>, like <u>light intensity</u> or <u>humidity</u>, in the laboratory.

5) You can make a simple choice chamber using a <u>Petri dish</u>:

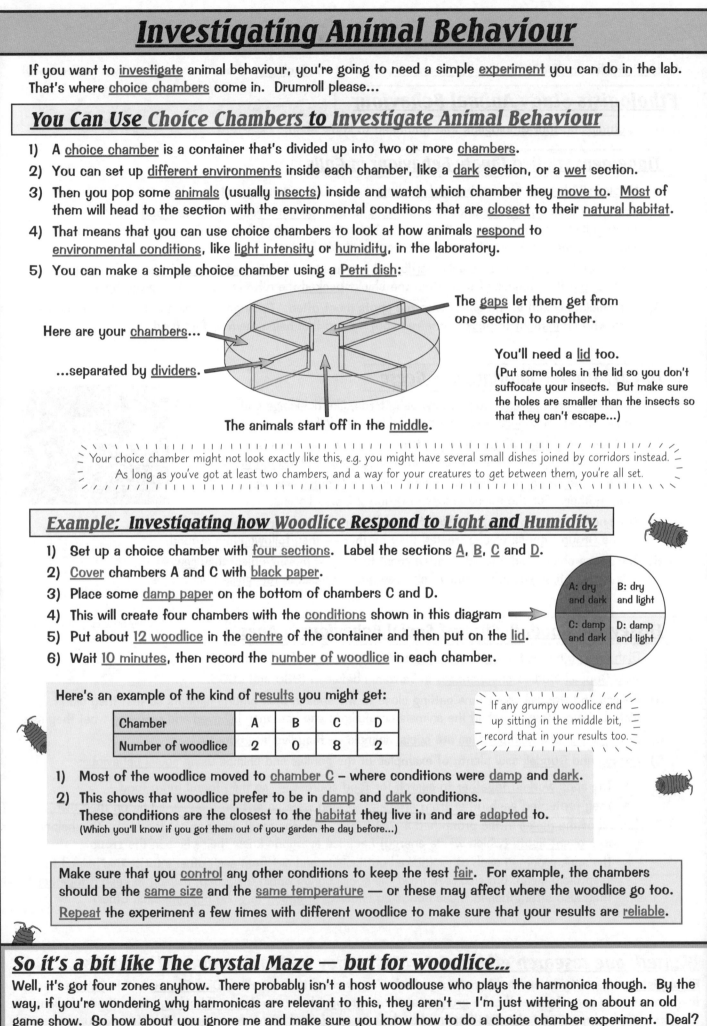

The <u>gaps</u> let them get from one section to another.

Here are your <u>chambers</u>...

...separated by <u>dividers</u>.

You'll need a <u>lid</u> too.
(Put some holes in the lid so you don't suffocate your insects. But make sure the holes are smaller than the insects so that they can't escape...)

The animals start off in the <u>middle</u>.

Your choice chamber might not look exactly like this, e.g. you might have several small dishes joined by corridors instead. As long as you've got at least two chambers, and a way for your creatures to get between them, you're all set.

Example: Investigating how <u>Woodlice Respond</u> to <u>Light and Humidity</u>

1) Set up a choice chamber with <u>four sections</u>. Label the sections <u>A</u>, <u>B</u>, <u>C</u> and <u>D</u>.

2) <u>Cover</u> chambers A and C with <u>black paper</u>.

3) Place some <u>damp paper</u> on the bottom of chambers C and D.

4) This will create four chambers with the <u>conditions</u> shown in this diagram ➡

5) Put about <u>12 woodlice</u> in the <u>centre</u> of the container and then put on the <u>lid</u>.

6) Wait <u>10 minutes</u>, then record the <u>number of woodlice</u> in each chamber.

| A: dry and dark | B: dry and light |
| C: damp and dark | D: damp and light |

Here's an example of the kind of <u>results</u> you might get:

Chamber	A	B	C	D
Number of woodlice	2	0	8	2

If any grumpy woodlice end up sitting in the middle bit, record that in your results too.

1) Most of the woodlice moved to <u>chamber C</u> – where conditions were <u>damp</u> and <u>dark</u>.

2) This shows that woodlice prefer to be in <u>damp</u> and <u>dark</u> conditions.
These conditions are the closest to the <u>habitat</u> they live in and are <u>adapted</u> to.
(Which you'll know if you got them out of your garden the day before...)

Make sure that you <u>control</u> any other conditions to keep the test <u>fair</u>. For example, the chambers should be the <u>same size</u> and the <u>same temperature</u> — or these may affect where the woodlice go too. <u>Repeat</u> the experiment a few times with different woodlice to make sure that your results are <u>reliable</u>.

So it's a bit like The Crystal Maze — but for woodlice...

Well, it's got four zones anyhow. There probably isn't a host woodlouse who plays the harmonica though. By the way, if you're wondering why harmonicas are relevant to this, they aren't — I'm just wittering on about an old game show. So how about you ignore me and make sure you know how to do a choice chamber experiment. Deal?

Mating Behaviour

Ooh... mating and reproduction. No need to get all shy though, it's only about moths and lions doing it.

To Reproduce Sexually You Need to Find and Select a Mate

Finding a potential mate is fairly easy if an animal lives in a social group, but many
animals live in <u>isolation</u> and only spend time with others during the <u>mating season</u>.
They have to behave in a way that will allow them to find a <u>mate</u>.
Here are a few facts about finding a mate:

1) A lot of animals make some sort of <u>song</u> or <u>call</u> to attract a mate, as in many birds,
    whales and frogs. It is usually the <u>males</u> who make the call, to <u>attract</u> females to them.

2) Some <u>insects</u> use chemicals called <u>pheromones</u> as sexual attractants, but here it's usually
    the <u>female</u> who produces the signal. In <u>moths</u>, the pheromone can be detected by a male
    several kilometres away, and he can follow the <u>trail</u> to find the female.

3) Sometimes, males actually <u>fight</u> each other and only the winners get to mate, e.g. <u>deer</u> do this.
    Obviously, it wouldn't be good for the species if lots of males got injured or even killed, so
    instead of real fighting, the fights often involve <u>displays</u>. These displays <u>indicate strength</u> and
    give the weaker male a chance to <u>back away</u>.

4) <u>Courtship displays</u> usually involve the male doing a special display to impress the female.
    They involve things like exaggerated <u>posturing</u>, <u>dancing</u> and showing brightly <u>coloured</u> parts of
    the anatomy. Courtship displays are <u>species-specific</u> — so the female knows she is mating with
    a male of the <u>right species</u>. There is often a link between the impressiveness of the display and
    the <u>fertility</u> of the male. In the mandrill, a mammal with a very brightly coloured face and bum,
    the <u>brightness</u> of the colours is linked with the level of <u>testosterone</u>, the male sex hormone.

> Because the <u>female</u> of most species puts much more <u>effort</u> into child-rearing than
> the male, it's important that she doesn't mate with a male of a closely related
> species. If she did, she'd produce <u>infertile</u> offspring and all her efforts to pass on
> her genes would be wasted. It's also best if the male is <u>strong</u> and <u>fertile</u>, as this
> ensures that the next generation will have the best possible chance of <u>survival</u>.
>
> This is why <u>females</u> tend to <u>select</u> a mate, and males have to show that they're
> <u>worthy</u> of selection. It's not so important for males to be choosy — their job
> is simply to mate with as many females as they can.

The mandrill: look at his silly nose.
(Shame you can't see his bum.)

Most Animals Have More Than One Mate

<u>Monogamy</u> (staying with just <u>one</u> mate) occurs mostly in <u>birds</u>. It's pretty <u>rare</u> in the rest of the
animal kingdom. <u>Most</u> animals have <u>more than one</u> mate, but mating patterns <u>vary</u> between species:

1) In most species, the male takes <u>no part</u> in the birth or care of the young, so there's no reason for him
    to stick around. Instead he'll go off and mate with <u>other females</u> during the <u>same</u> mating season.

2) In some species (some birds, for instance), he'll mate with <u>one</u> female <u>each</u> season,
    though not necessarily the same one from year to year.

3) In some mammals (e.g. the lion), a male may have a <u>group</u> of females which he
    stays with, but mates with <u>all</u> of them. These females are known as his '<u>harem</u>'.

4) The few animals that are <u>monogamous</u> include the following:
    *   Birds — albatross, bald eagle, swan, mallard, raven, penguins and parrots
    *   Mammals — gibbons and prairie voles

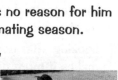

Male sea lion with his harem

Showing your bum will only attract the police...

So then... what about <u>humans</u>? Some cultures are <u>not monogamous</u>. In these it's fine for men to have more
than one wife. Other cultures have a kind of 'enforced monogamy', where society or religion say that you should
have one partner only. In these cultures you find that there's a lot of <u>secret infidelity</u>.

Parenting Behaviour

Our parents often look after us for our first eighteen years — that's crazy compared to most animals.

Some Animals Look After Their Young

Most animals give birth to their young and then leave them to <u>fend for themselves</u>. If they lay eggs, they may <u>incubate</u> and protect the eggs until they are hatched, and then <u>leave</u>. However, in some species, one or both parents look after the young in a variety of ways for different lengths of time. The care may involve <u>protecting</u> them, <u>feeding</u> them and <u>teaching</u> them basic skills. This level of care is mostly seen in <u>birds</u> and <u>mammals</u>, although <u>crocodiles</u> and some <u>fish</u> also care for their young.

PROTECTION

Protection may just involve one parent <u>staying</u> with the young to keep them together and to fend off <u>predators</u>. In some cases, protection is helped by the construction of elaborate <u>nests</u> to enclose the young. The <u>weaver bird</u> weaves strands of leaves and twigs into a ball, sometimes with a long tube attached, which makes it difficult for predators to take, or even notice, the young.

FEEDING

If a species both <u>feeds</u> and <u>protects</u> its young, this usually means that <u>both parents</u> need to be involved — one to stay with the young, the other to get food.

TEACHING SKILLS

Certain behaviours are <u>innate</u> and baby animals will learn them without being taught — e.g. <u>walking</u> in mammals, and <u>flying</u> in birds. Other skills need to be <u>taught</u>. Birds called <u>oystercatchers</u> get food by <u>opening mussels</u>, a difficult task which an experienced bird can do in less than a minute, but one that takes months for the young to learn. <u>Human</u> babies need to be taught a whole range of skills from how to get dressed to eating with a knife and fork (or chopsticks). Apart from in humans, where <u>language</u> is very useful in teaching, babies usually learn by simply <u>imitating</u> their parents' behaviour.

Looking After Young Increases Their Survival

Looking after the young puts the mother (in particular) at <u>risk</u>. <u>Food</u> has to be <u>shared</u>, and a lot of <u>time</u> has to be spent with the eggs and baby animals. If the parents protect the young from predators, they <u>decrease</u> their own chances of <u>escaping</u>. Here's why they bother:

1) Parental care greatly <u>increases</u> the proportion of the young that <u>survive</u>. In birds that care for their eggs and young, about <u>25%</u> of the eggs will produce adult birds. This is high compared to most animals — for example, fewer than <u>one in a million</u> cod eggs survive to become adult fish.

2) Looking after young is <u>less risky</u> for the mother than being <u>pregnant</u>, which puts <u>strain</u> on her body and makes it more difficult to <u>escape predators</u>. If animals <u>care</u> for their young, it means they can give birth to a <u>less developed</u> baby, and so have a <u>shorter pregnancy</u> and spend less time at risk. This only applies to <u>mammals</u> though, as the embryos in birds' eggs are undeveloped when laid.

3) From the species' point of view, it is the survival of an animal's <u>genes</u> into the next generation that is important, rather than the survival of the animal itself. This may be why an animal will <u>risk death</u> (and the loss of <u>one</u> copy of its genes) to protect, for example, <u>four</u> offspring, which all contain its genes.

Go and thank your parents for their efforts right now...

Think about all the things that human <u>parents</u> and <u>carers</u> do — they keep their kids well-fed, clean, warm, happy, healthy and safe, and they keep doing it for years. They most likely hold down a job in order to pay for all the things that kids need too. And all a <u>cod</u> does is lay some eggs and leave. Pah.

Plant Communication and Co-evolution

Plants don't talk to the animals like Dr Doolittle, but they do give out signals that other organisms respond to. Plants and animals have also co-evolved, which have left them with some pretty nifty adaptations...

Plants Can Release Chemicals to Attract Insects

Plants send out chemical signals to:

ATTRACT POLLINATORS Lots of flowers are scented — they release smelly chemicals to attract insects. The insects come to the flower looking for sugary nectar. While they're there, some pollen gets stuck to them. When they fly away they carry the pollen to other plants.

ATTRACT INSECT PREDATORS Some plants release chemicals into the air when an insect pest is eating them. These chemicals attract a predator insect that feeds on the pest. The predator eats the pest but not the plant. So the predator gets food and the plant gets rid of the pest.

Plants Can Release Chemicals to Warn Other Plants

1) Some plants have leaves that can release chemicals into the air if they are being eaten by insects.

2) When another leaf on the plant detects the signal, it makes chemicals that make the leaf harder to digest.

3) When other nearby plants detect the signal they prepare themselves for attack in the same way.

signal

nasty leaves

all tasty leaves

Some Plants and Animals Have Co-evolved

Co-evolution is where two organisms evolve in response to each other.
There are a couple of examples you need to know:

① Plants and their insect pollinators

1) It's an advantage for an insect if it can reach the nectar in a particular type of flower that other insects can't reach — it will be the only insect that can get the nectar from that type of flower.

2) It's also an advantage for a plant if only one type of insect can get nectar from its flowers — that insect is more likely to visit other flowers of the same type and pollinate them.

3) So some plants and their insect pollinators have co-evolved. For example, some orchids have evolved really deep nectar stores and are pollinated by a type of moth that has evolved a really long mouth part to reach its nectar.

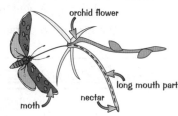

orchid flower

long mouth part

nectar

moth

② Plants and insects that eat them

1) It's an advantage if a plant can produce nasty chemicals so that most insects can't eat it — it'll get munched on much less often.

2) It's an advantage for an insect if it can eat a plant that other insects can't — it gets more food.

3) So some insects have evolved to eat poisonous plants, e.g. caterpillars of the cinnabar moth eat ragwort, which is poisonous to other animals.

My feet evolved in response to my shoes — it was a kind of toe-evolution...

So, this co-evolution lark explains how you can end up with some really strange species that seem to be really well-adapted to a quirk in another species. Make sure you learn the two types of co-evolution above.

Fossil Evidence for Human Evolution

Here's one way in which we've found out what our ancestors were like... (it explains a lot).

Fossils *Give Us Clues About What* Human Ancestors *Were Like...*

1) <u>Chimpanzees</u> are our closest living relatives. Evidence from <u>fossils</u> suggests that humans and chimpanzees evolved from a <u>common ancestor</u> that existed around 6 million years ago.

2) Human beings and their ancestors are known as <u>hominids</u>. Fossils of several different <u>hominid species</u> have been found — they have characteristics that are <u>between</u> apes and humans.

3) By looking at <u>hominid fossils</u>, you can see how humans have <u>evolved</u> over time...

'Ardi' is a Fossil Hominid 4.4 Million Years Old

<u>Ardi</u> is a <u>fossil</u> of the species *Ardipithecus ramidus*. She was found in Ethiopia and is <u>4.4 million years old</u>. Ardi's features are a <u>mixture</u> of those found in humans and in apes:

1) The structure of her <u>feet</u> suggests she <u>climbed trees</u> — she had an <u>ape-like big toe</u> to grasp branches.

2) She also had <u>long arms</u> and <u>short legs</u> — more like an <u>ape</u> than a <u>human</u>.

3) Her <u>brain size</u> was about the same as a <u>chimpanzee</u>.

4) But the structure of her legs suggests that she <u>walked upright</u> like a human. The structure of her <u>hand bones</u> also suggests she didn't use her <u>hands</u> to help her <u>walk</u> (like <u>apes</u> do).

'Lucy' is a Fossil Hominid 3.2 Million Years Old

<u>Lucy</u> is a fossil of the species *Australopithecus afarensis*. She was found in Ethiopia and is <u>3.2 million years old</u>. Lucy also has a <u>mixture</u> of human features and ape features, but she is <u>more human-like</u> than Ardi.

1) Lucy had <u>arched feet</u>, more adapted to walking than climbing, and no ape-like big toe.

2) The size of her <u>arms</u> and <u>legs</u> was <u>between</u> what you would expect to find in apes and humans.

3) Her <u>brain</u> was <u>slightly larger</u> than Ardi's but still similar in size to a <u>chimp's brain</u>.

4) The structure of Lucy's leg bones and feet suggest she also <u>walked upright</u>, but more <u>efficiently</u> than Ardi.

Leakey and His Team Found Fossil Hominids 1.6 Million Years Old

In 1984 scientist <u>Richard Leakey</u> organised an expedition to Kenya to look for <u>hominid fossils</u>. Leakey and his team discovered <u>many important fossils</u> of different *Australopithecus* and *Homo* species.

One of their finds was <u>Turkana Boy</u> — he is a fossil skeleton of the species *Homo erectus* and is about <u>1.6 million years old</u>. He has a <u>mixture</u> of human and ape-like features, but is <u>more human-like</u> than Lucy.

1) His <u>short arms</u> and <u>long legs</u> are much more like a <u>human</u> than an <u>ape</u>.

2) His <u>brain size</u> was <u>much larger</u> than Lucy's — similar to <u>human</u> brain size.

3) The structure of his legs and feet suggest he was even better adapted to <u>walking upright</u> than Lucy.

...And Can be Put on a Timeline to Show Human Evolution

So you know that the *Ardipithicus* and *Australopithecus* species were more <u>ape-like</u>, compared to the *Homo* species, which are <u>human-like</u>. They can all be put on a time line, showing how <u>humans</u> have <u>evolved</u>:

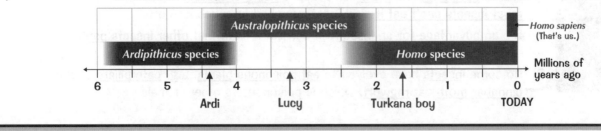

Hang on a minute — how do they know her name was Lucy?

Maybe her name was sewn into her coat. Anyway, you need to <u>know</u> the <u>names</u> and <u>ages</u> of these three fossils, plus how their <u>features</u> were becoming more <u>human-like</u> over time. Typical. Bet Lucy never had to revise...

More Evidence for Human Evolution

As our ancestors evolved, both the <u>tools</u> they used and their <u>DNA</u> changed.

Development of Stone Tools Provides Evidence For Human Evolution

The different <u>Homo</u> species (see page 94) continued to <u>evolve</u>. You can tell this because they started using <u>stone tools</u> and these gradually became <u>more complex</u> (so their <u>brains</u> must have been getting <u>larger</u>):

Homo species	Tool use
Homo habilis (2.5-1.5 million years ago)	Made simple stone tools called pebble tools by hitting rocks together to make sharp flakes. These could be used to scrape meat from bones or crack bones open.
Homo erectus (2-0.3 million years ago)	Sculpted rocks into shapes to produce more complex tools like simple hand-axes. These could be used to hunt, dig, chop and scrape meat from bones.
Homo neanderthalis (300 000-25 000 years ago)	More complex tools. Evidence of flint tools, pointed tools and wooden spears.
Homo sapiens (200 000-present)	Flint tools widely used. Pointed tools including arrowheads, fish hooks, buttons and needles appeared around 50 000 years ago.

When an ancient stone tool is found, there are several <u>different ways</u> scientists can work out <u>how old it is</u>:

1) By using <u>stratigraphy</u> — the study of <u>rock layers</u>. <u>Older</u> rock layers are normally found <u>below</u> younger layers, so tools in <u>deeper</u> layers are <u>older</u>.

2) By <u>dating</u> any <u>fossils</u> found with the stone tools.

3) By using <u>carbon-14 dating</u> to date any <u>material</u> found with it that is made from carbon, e.g. a wood handle.

Dating a stone tool isn't always very accurate, e.g. rock layers can move over time.

Mitochondrial DNA Also Provides Evidence For Human Evolution

1) <u>Mitochondria</u> have a <u>small piece of DNA</u> inside them. (It's separate from the DNA in the nucleus.)

2) Mitochondrial DNA is <u>inherited</u> from the <u>mother</u> (so you got yours from your mum, she got hers from her mum etc). This means it's <u>not mixed</u> with DNA from the father.

3) Scientists use mitochondrial DNA to study human evolution — the <u>more different</u> two mitochondrial DNA samples are, the <u>further back</u> they shared a common ancestor.

4) It turns out that <u>everyone</u> on the planet has <u>similar</u> mitochondrial DNA.

5) This shows that everyone is descended from <u>one woman</u>. Scientists call her '<u>Mitochondrial Eve</u>'.

6) Some bits of mitochondrial DNA do vary from person to person due to <u>mutations</u>. These mutations occur often — mitochondrial DNA has a <u>high mutation rate</u>.

7) Scientists have been able to analyse the mutations in samples of mitochondrial DNA and work out that Mitochondrial Eve was an <u>African woman</u> who lived <u>200 000 years ago</u>. (She's also known as '<u>African Eve</u>'.)

This doesn't mean she was the only woman around at the time though.

8) The discovery of Mitochondrial Eve meant that <u>Homo sapiens</u> must have <u>evolved in Africa</u>, then <u>spread</u> from there <u>across the world</u>. (Some people used to think that Homo sapiens evolved from Homo erectus and Homo neanderthalis that had already spread from Africa to parts of Europe and Asia).

9) Nuclear DNA (DNA in the nucleus) is also used to study human evolution and migration. However, <u>mitochondrial DNA</u> can be <u>more useful</u> for this than nuclear DNA because:

- There are <u>lots of mitochondria</u> in a cell, so there are <u>lots of copies</u> of <u>mitochondrial DNA</u>.
- Mitochondrial DNA is less likely to <u>degrade</u> over time.

Dating fossils — I might have better luck with them...

So, as well as fossils providing evidence for how humans have evolved, there's evidence from <u>stone tools</u> and <u>mitochondrial DNA</u> too. And mitochondrial DNA proves that we (Homo sapiens) evolved in <u>Africa</u> and then <u>migrated</u> to other areas of the world. Clever, innit? Handily, there's more about migration on the next page....

Climate Change and Human Behaviour

Humans beings are a pretty adaptable lot — you can tell by all the different areas of the world we survive in.

Migration Caused Changes In Human Behaviour

1) As humans <u>migrated</u> out of Africa (see previous page) they encountered lots of <u>new environments</u>.

2) As they came into contact with these new environments, they gradually <u>changed their behaviour</u> to <u>survive</u>.

3) They first moved to <u>coastal areas</u> of the Near East and Asia, then on to the <u>hotter</u> lands that would become Australia, and finally to Europe, with its <u>cold</u> climate.

THE COAST OF THE NEAR EAST AND ASIA

New settlers here changed their <u>diet</u> — they started to eat <u>shellfish</u> and other <u>seafood</u>.
This also meant that they had to invent new <u>stone tools</u> to get the shellfish out of their shells.

AUSTRALIA

Rainforest settlers started to eat the <u>fruit</u> that grew in the <u>trees</u>.
This meant inventing <u>new tools</u> to reach it, e.g. <u>long sticks</u> to knock the fruit down.

EUROPE

- The settlers <u>changed their diet</u> to include the <u>new plants and animals</u> they found.
- Many of the animal species they found were <u>large animals</u>. This meant they had to devise <u>new methods</u> of <u>hunting</u> so that they could hunt in <u>groups</u>. It also meant making <u>new tools</u>, like knives and saws, to prepare larger animals for eating.
- Because the climate was colder, they started to <u>build more shelters</u>.
- Humans settling in these cold areas began to use <u>animal skins</u> (especially fur) to make themselves <u>warm clothes</u>.

Humans have Changed their Behaviour to Survive an Ice Age

<u>Ice ages</u> are long periods of <u>very cold climate</u> during which <u>ice sheets</u> and <u>glaciers</u> spread across most of the Earth. There have been several major ice ages in Earth's history. To survive the last ice age, <u>human beings</u> had to cope with <u>extremely cold</u> conditions. Here are some examples of how they did this:

1) They began to <u>build</u> more <u>shelters</u> (or seek shelter in <u>caves</u>).
2) Humans used <u>fire</u>, e.g. to <u>heat</u> their shelters.
3) They <u>wore</u> more <u>warm clothing</u> made from <u>skins</u> and <u>fur</u>.
4) <u>Hunting</u> for animals <u>increased</u>.
5) They began to <u>make</u> and <u>use</u> more <u>tools</u> (because they were building, making clothes and hunting more).
6) <u>Cooperation</u> and <u>communication</u> increased as groups of humans <u>worked together</u> to survive. <u>Language</u> also developed to help groups communicate and pass knowledge on to others.

Using language to pass knowledge on — what a good idea...

The basic idea of this page is that if you <u>move</u> somewhere <u>new</u> (that has <u>different conditions</u>) you change your <u>behaviour</u> to cope with it, e.g. by eating different <u>food</u> and wearing different <u>clothes</u>. Makes sense really. And, in the same way, if conditions change <u>where you are</u>, you have to change your behaviour too.

Revision Summary for B3 Topic 2

What an interesting topic. I don't know about you, but I'm fascinated by this sort of stuff. There are so many things in this section that you could try out at home — conditioning your pets to salivate when you ring a bell, habituating your parents to loud music, persuading geese to follow you round, using long sticks to hit fruit... I could go on...

Anyway, I digress. Back to the important issue of finding out how much of this stuff you've taken in. Answer all of the questions. If you get stuck on any of them go back and read the relevant bits again, until you can answer them — it's the only way to make sure that it's all in your head.

1) Define 'behaviour'. Why do we need behaviour? What influences it?
2) Name three reflex actions. What are reflexes for?
3) What's the process called when birds learn to ignore scarecrows? Give another example.
4) What is imprinting?
5) Give a definition of classical conditioning. Make sure you use the word 'passively'.
6) Which type of conditioning did Ivan Pavlov study? What experiment did Pavlov do?
7) Which type of conditioning is happening when someone rewards a dog for sitting down when told?
8) Give three ways in which conditioning is used to train animals.
9) Give three reasons why it's beneficial for animals who live in a group to communicate with each other.
10) Name three species which communicate through sound.
11) What are pheromones? What uses them and why would they want to?
12) What is the 'waggle dance'? Name two other visual signals used by animals.
13) Name an ethologist who studied innate behaviour in gulls.
14) Describe how Lorenz studied imprinting in geese and what he discovered.
15) Describe two types of behaviour that Fossey and Goodall observed whilst studying apes.
16) What is a choice chamber?
17) Briefly describe an experiment you could do to find out whether ladybirds prefer a dark environment or a light environment.
18) Why are courtship displays species-specific?
19) Why do females tend to be choosy when it comes to selecting a mate?
20) Describe some of the mating patterns found in the animal kingdom. How common is monogamy?
21) Apart from feeding and protecting, what do some animals do as part of caring for their young?
22) Briefly explain the evolutionary argument for why mammals care for their young.
23) Give two reasons why plants might release chemicals that attract insects.
24) Describe one way in which plants and insects have co-evolved.
25) Name two ape-like features that 'Ardi' the fossil hominid had.
26) How old is 'Lucy' the fossil hominid?
27) Explain how stone tools provide evidence for human evolution.
28) Give one way in which stone tools can be dated.
29) Why is mitochondrial DNA more useful than nuclear DNA for studying human evolution?
30) Describe one way in which the humans who migrated to Europe changed their behaviour.
31) Give three ways in which humans changed their behaviour to survive the last ice age.

Large-scale Growth of Microorganisms

Welcome to the <u>biotechnology section</u>. You're going to have fun here, I can tell. Biotechnology isn't anything fancy — 'bio' just means life, and 'technology' means, well... technology. Here's a slightly better definition:

> <u>Biotechnology</u> means <u>using living organisms</u> (especially microorganisms) to produce <u>useful products</u> (e.g. food, medicines) or to provide people with <u>services</u> (e.g. waste management, water purification).

First up, you need to know how to <u>grow</u> loads and loads of <u>microorganisms</u>... it might come in handy one day.

Microorganisms are Grown in Fermenters on a Large Scale

A fermenter is a big container full of <u>liquid</u> 'culture medium' which microorganisms can <u>grow</u> and <u>reproduce</u> in. The fermenter needs to have the <u>right conditions</u> for the microorganisms to <u>grow</u> and produce their <u>useful product</u> on a large scale.

1) <u>Food</u> is provided in the liquid culture medium. Microorganisms need <u>carbohydrates</u> (sugars) as an energy source, plus <u>nitrates</u> (to make protein) and <u>vitamins</u> and <u>minerals</u>. More nutrients can be pumped in if needed.

2) Air is piped in to supply <u>oxygen</u> to the microorganisms (if they respire aerobically).

3) The microorganisms need to be kept at the <u>right temperature</u> for optimum growth. If it's <u>too cold</u> the growth rate will <u>slow down</u>. If it's <u>too hot</u> enzymes in the microorganisms will be denatured (destroyed) and growth will stop. The microorganisms produce <u>heat</u> by respiration, so the fermenters must be <u>cooled</u>. This is usually done with a <u>water jacket</u> which cold water is pumped through.

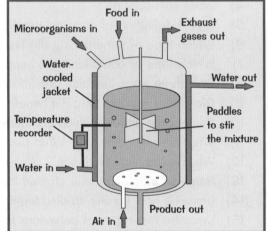

4) The <u>right pH</u> is needed for the microorganisms to thrive. Instruments are used to monitor this.

5) <u>Sterile (aseptic) conditions</u> are needed to <u>prevent contamination</u> from other microorganisms.

6) A <u>motorised stirrer</u> keeps the culture <u>well-mixed</u>, so <u>all</u> the microorganisms get enough oxygen and nutrients.

You Can Investigate the Effect of Different Factors on Yeast Growth

When yeast respires <u>anaerobically</u> it turns sugar into CO_2 and <u>alcohol</u>.
You can do an experiment to measure the <u>rate of CO_2 production</u> by yeast under <u>anaerobic conditions</u>:

1) Boil water in a test tube to get rid of any <u>dissolved oxygen</u>.

2) When it's cooled, dissolve a small amount of <u>sugar</u> and <u>yeast</u> in the water.

3) Add a layer of <u>paraffin</u> to keep out <u>oxygen</u>.

4) Attach a <u>bung</u> with a tube leading to a second test tube of <u>lime water</u>.

5) The <u>lime water</u> in the second tube lets you check that it's CO_2 being given off (the lime water will go <u>milky</u>).

6) Then you can <u>count the bubbles</u> produced in a certain time to measure the <u>rate</u> of CO_2 production.

<u>Compare</u> the rates of CO_2 production under <u>different conditions</u> to see the growth of yeast, e.g:

- Put the test tubes in <u>water baths</u> at different <u>temperatures</u> — yeast grows quickest at around <u>37 °C</u>. It grows <u>slower</u> at <u>lower</u> temperatures but will be <u>killed</u> at temperatures <u>higher</u> than about 48 °C.
- Vary the <u>pH</u> of the solution — yeast grows best at a <u>slightly acidic pH</u> (pH 4-4.5).
- Vary the <u>sugar concentration</u> — the <u>more sugar</u> available as an energy source, the <u>faster</u> yeast grows.

Culture medium — sounds very BBC Four to me...

<u>Fermenters</u> come in all shapes and sizes. Industrial ones can contain as much volume as a swimming pool. That really is an <u>awful lot of microorganisms</u>. Not that much fun to swim in though I imagine...

Microorganisms and Food

Microorganisms can be useful little critters — they're used to make all kinds of different foods.

Mycoprotein — Food from Fungi

1) Mycoprotein is used to make meat substitutes for vegetarian meals, e.g. Quorn™.
2) The fungus _Fusarium_ is grown in fermenters using glucose syrup as food.
3) The fungus respires aerobically, so it needs to be supplied with oxygen.
4) Mycoprotein has health benefits over meat — it contains more protein and fibre, and much less fat.

Mycoprotein is the squished fungi. Eeew...

Bacteria Ferment Milk to Produce Yoghurt

Fermentation is when microorganisms break sugars down to release energy — usually by anaerobic respiration. Yoghurt is basically fermented milk. Here's how it's made...

1) The equipment is sterilised to kill off any unwanted microorganisms.
2) The milk's pasteurised (see p.78), then cooled.
3) A starter culture of _Lactobacillus_ bacteria is added and the mixture is incubated (heated to about 40 °C) in a fermenter (see p.98).
4) The bacteria ferment the lactose sugar in the milk to form lactic acid. Lactic acid causes the milk to clot, and solidify into yoghurt.
5) Finally, flavours (e.g. fruit) and colours are sometimes added and the yoghurt is packaged.

Investigating the Effect of Different Factors on Yoghurt Making

Here's how to investigate the effect of temperature on yoghurt production:

1) Add 25 cm^3 of milk to 5 sterile boiling tubes. Pasteurise and then cool the milk.
2) Add 1 cm^3 of yoghurt starter culture (_Lactobacillus_ bacteria) to each boiling tube and stir gently.
3) Incubate the tubes for 5 hours at 5 different temperatures — 20 °C, 30 °C, 40 °C, 50 °C and 60 °C.
4) To see how successful yoghurt production is, you can measure the pH of the tubes after 5 hours:

- As yoghurt's made, pH decreases from about pH 7 to pH 4 because of the lactic acid that's produced. (The reaction slows down at around pH 4 because the bacteria are sensitive to acidic conditions.)
- The pH should be around pH 4 for the tube incubated at 40 °C, because this is the best temperature for the optimum growth of the bacteria.
- The pH should be higher (less acidic) at temperatures lower than 40 °C as the growth rate is slower.
- The pH should stay at 7 at higher temperatures because these kill the bacteria, so you get no yoghurt.

5) You can look at the effect of a different variable on yeast growth, but keep any other variables the same.

Advantages of Using Microorganisms for Food Production

1) Microorganisms like bacteria and fungi can grow very quickly. They can grow miles quicker than plants or animals... which is good if you're using them to make food.
2) They're also easy to look after. All that's needed is something to grow them in, food, oxygen, and the right temperature.
3) Another plus is that food can be produced whether the climate is hot or cold. Many places in the world are pretty unsuitable for farming crops or animals, e.g. Siberia and parts of Africa. Microorganisms can be used to produce food anywhere if you have the right equipment.
4) Microorganisms can use waste products from agriculture and industry as food for their life processes.
5) This often makes using microorganisms cheaper than other methods.

So bacteria aren't always the bad guys...

It seems weird. Microorganisms in food can make you ill — that's why you should wash your hands before touching food and make sure meat is cooked thoroughly — but without them, we wouldn't have yummy foods like yoghurt.

Using Enzymes

Enzymes are molecules made of <u>protein</u>, which <u>speed up (catalyse) chemical reactions</u> in living organisms. Scientists know a good thing when they see it, and enzymes are now used for all sorts of stuff...

Enzymes are Used in Biological Washing Powders

1) Some stains are caused by <u>soluble</u> chemicals and so they <u>wash out</u> easily in water. Stubborn stains contain <u>insoluble chemicals</u> like starch, proteins and fats. They don't wash out with just water.

2) <u>Non-biological washing powders</u> (detergents) contain <u>chemicals</u> that break up <u>stains</u> on your clothes.

3) <u>Biological washing powders</u> contain the same chemicals as non-biological ones, but also contain a mixture of <u>enzymes</u> which break down the stubborn stains.

Stain	Sources of stain	Enzymes	Product
Carbohydrate	Jam, chocolate	Amylases	Simple sugars
Lipid (fats)	Butter, oil	Lipases	Fatty acids and glycerol
Protein	Blood, grass	Proteases	Amino acids

The <u>products</u> of the enzyme-controlled reactions are <u>soluble in water</u> and so can be easily washed out of the material.

4) Biological washing powders are <u>more effective</u> at working at <u>low temperatures</u> (e.g. 30 °C) than non-biological washing powders.

5) The enzymes <u>work best</u> at <u>pH 7</u> (neutral). Tap water is usually about pH 7, but in areas with very hard water (water containing high levels of calcium) it might be alkaline, which can damage the enzymes.

6) You can buy <u>special stain removers</u> (e.g. for wine, blood or oil). Some of these are just special solvents, but some contain <u>specific enzymes</u> that will break down the stain.

Some Enzymes are Used to Make Foods

<u>Enzymes</u> can also play a part in <u>food production</u>. You need to know these <u>two examples</u>:

CHYMOSIN

1) <u>Cheese</u> is made using a substance called <u>rennet</u>.

2) Rennet is <u>traditionally</u> obtained from the <u>lining of a calf's stomach</u>. It contains an <u>enzyme</u> called <u>chymosin</u>, which <u>clots</u> the <u>milk</u>.

3) But <u>vegetarians</u> probably don't want to eat cheese made with rennet from animals...
...so <u>vegetarian cheese</u> is made using chymosin from <u>genetically modified microorganisms</u>.

4) Basically, the genes responsible for chymosin were isolated from calf stomach cells and put into <u>yeast</u> cells. These were then grown on an industrial scale to produce chymosin.

INVERTASE

1) The enzyme <u>invertase</u> (or <u>sucrase</u>) is used in the manufacture of sweets and other foods.

2) Invertase converts the <u>sucrose</u> (a sugar) into <u>glucose</u> and <u>fructose</u> (different types of sugar) which taste <u>sweeter</u>. This means that <u>less sugar</u> is needed for the <u>same sweetness</u> — meaning manufacturers can save <u>money</u> and produce <u>lower-calorie sweet foods</u>.

3) Invertase is naturally produced by a yeast called <u>Saccharomyces cerevisiae</u>.

Stubborn stains — not just dirty, but grumpy...

Not everyone can use <u>biological washing powders</u>. Some of the enzymes remain on the clothes and can <u>irritate sensitive skin</u>, making it sore and itchy. Sensitive people have to use <u>non-biological</u> powders.

Enzyme Experiments

So enzymes are used in industry, big deal, yadda yadda. What you <u>really</u> want to know is how you can get your hands on the stuff and <u>do it yourself</u>. Well luckily, you need to know all about these <u>experiments</u>...

Immobilising Enzymes Makes Them Easier to Remove

1) When enzymes are used to speed up reactions, they end up <u>dissolved in the mixture</u> with the substrates and products — and can be <u>difficult to remove</u>.

2) Many industrial processes use <u>immobilised enzymes</u>, which <u>don't</u> need to be <u>separated out</u> from the mixture after the reaction has taken place.

3) Immobilised enzymes are <u>attached</u> to an <u>insoluble material</u>, e.g. <u>fibres</u>. Or they're encapsulated in <u>alginate beads</u> (alginate is a gel-like substance). The insoluble material with attached enzymes can be washed and <u>reused</u>.

enzyme molecule
encapsulated within
a bead of alginate

Immobilised Enzymes Can be Used to Make Lactose-Free Milk

1) The sugar <u>lactose</u> is naturally found in <u>milk</u> (and yoghurt). It's broken down in your digestive system by the <u>enzyme lactase</u>. This produces <u>glucose</u> and <u>galactose</u>, which are then <u>absorbed</u> into the blood.

2) Some people <u>lack the enzyme lactase</u>. If they drink milk the lactose isn't broken down and gut <u>bacteria</u> feed on it, causing <u>abdominal pain</u>, <u>wind</u> and <u>diarrhoea</u> — these people are <u>lactose intolerant</u>.

3) <u>Lactose-free milk</u> can be produced using <u>immobilised lactase</u>. Here's how you'd do it in the lab:

Immobilising the lactase
1) Mix <u>sodium alginate</u> and <u>lactase</u> together in a <u>syringe</u>.
2) Add the mixture <u>one drop at a time</u> to a beaker of <u>calcium chloride</u>.
3) You should find that <u>beads</u> form (the lactase is <u>immobilised</u> in the beads). Leave them to <u>harden</u> for a few minutes, then use a tea strainer to <u>separate</u> them from the calcium chloride solution.

Setting up a column of immobilised lactase
1) Put some <u>nylon gauze</u> in a syringe and attach a <u>tap</u> to the end (see diagram).
2) Add those lovely little <u>beads</u> that you've just made to the <u>syringe</u>.

Making the lactose-free milk
1) Use a <u>glucose test strip</u> to see if there's any <u>glucose present</u> in a beaker of <u>milk</u>.
2) <u>Slowly add the milk</u> to the syringe. Collect the <u>treated milk</u> in a small beaker.
3) Test the <u>glucose content</u> of the <u>treated milk</u> and <u>compare</u> it to the <u>untreated milk</u>.

untreated milk
lactase beads
nylon gauze
tap
treated milk

You should find that <u>before</u> treatment, the test strip <u>won't change colour</u> because there's <u>no glucose</u> in the milk. But in the <u>treated</u> milk it <u>will change colour</u>, showing that the lactose has been converted to glucose.

Pectinase is Used to Extract Apple Juice

The enzyme <u>pectinase</u> is used in <u>fruit juice extraction</u>. It breaks down <u>pectin</u> (a part of the cell wall in apples and oranges), causing the cell to <u>release</u> its juice. Here's how you can do a similar sort of thing:

1) Chop up an <u>apple</u> into <u>small chunks</u> and divide the chunks into <u>two beakers</u>.
2) Add <u>pectinase solution</u> to one of the beakers and add the same volume of <u>water</u> to the other, then <u>stir</u>.
3) <u>Incubate</u> the beakers in a <u>water bath</u> at <u>40°C</u>, for about <u>15 minutes</u>.
4) Then <u>filter</u> the contents of both beakers and <u>record</u> the volume of <u>juice</u> that you get from each.
5) You should find that you get <u>much more juice</u> from the beaker containing <u>pectinase</u> than the one with water.

I wish I could immobilise my little brother...

... that'd make him easier to remove... ahem. Make sure you know what <u>immobilised enzymes</u> are, <u>why</u> they're useful and how you can use them to make <u>lactose-free milk</u>. Then learn about <u>pectinase</u>. Then put your feet up.

Genetically Modifying Organisms

You met genetic engineering (another kind of biotechnology) on page 46. But you need more details now...

Bacteria can be Engineered to Produce Human Insulin

Genetic engineering is cutting a useful gene out of one organism and pasting it into to another. You know that the human insulin gene can be stuck into bacteria so that they make insulin — now you need a bit more detail:

1) A plasmid (a loop of DNA) is removed from a bacterium.

2) The insulin gene is cut out of a human chromosome using a restriction enzyme. Restriction enzymes recognise specific sequences of DNA and cut the DNA at these points. The cut leaves one of the DNA strands with unpaired bases — this is called a 'sticky end'.

3) The plasmid is cut open using the same restriction enzyme — leaving the same sticky ends.

4) The plasmid and the human insulin gene are mixed together.

5) Ligase (an enzyme) is added. This joins the sticky ends together to produce recombinant DNA (two different bits of DNA stuck together).

6) The recombinant DNA is inserted into bacterium.

7) The modified bacterium is grown in a fermenter. You end up with millions of bacteria that produce insulin for people with diabetes.

human insulin gene

sticky ends

plasmid

Restriction enzymes cut the gene out and cut open the plasmid...

sticky ends

...ligase joins the two bits of DNA together...

... and the recombinant DNA is inserted into the bacteria.

The bacteria are grown like mad in a fermenter.

Insulin

Bacteria that contain the gene for human insulin are transgenic — this means that they contain a gene transferred from another species. You can get transgenic plants too...

Agrobacterium Tumefaciens is Used to Genetically Modify Plants

1) To make GM plants, scientists often use a bacterium called *Agrobacterium tumefaciens*. This is a pathogen that invades plant cells and inserts its genes into the plant's DNA.

2) If other genes are added to this bacterium, then those genes are taken along too. Works a treat.

3) The *Agrobacterium tumefaciens* bacterium acts as a vector. ➤ A vector is a carrier that's used to insert DNA into other organisms.

4) For example, here's how you make a herbicide-resistant plant...

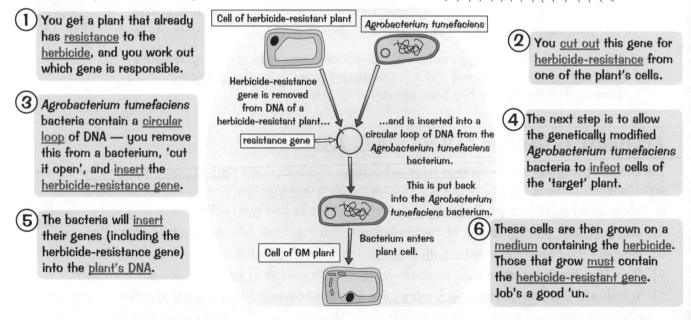

① You get a plant that already has resistance to the herbicide, and you work out which gene is responsible.

Cell of herbicide-resistant plant

Agrobacterium tumefaciens

② You cut out this gene for herbicide-resistance from one of the plant's cells.

Herbicide-resistance gene is removed from DNA of a herbicide-resistant plant...

resistance gene

...and is inserted into a circular loop of DNA from the *Agrobacterium tumefaciens* bacterium.

③ *Agrobacterium tumefaciens* bacteria contain a circular loop of DNA — you remove this from a bacterium, 'cut it open', and insert the herbicide-resistance gene.

This is put back into the *Agrobacterium tumefaciens* bacterium.

④ The next step is to allow the genetically modified *Agrobacterium tumefaciens* bacteria to infect cells of the 'target' plant.

⑤ The bacteria will insert their genes (including the herbicide-resistance gene) into the plant's DNA.

Cell of GM plant

Bacterium enters plant cell.

⑥ These cells are then grown on a medium containing the herbicide. Those that grow must contain the herbicide-resistant gene. Job's a good 'un.

Using GM bacteria to make GM plants... genius...

Genetically engineer a bacterium, then use that to genetically engineer a plant — cunning. GM crops are controversial (see p.103), but if they're as good as some people say, they may help with all sorts of problems.

More on GM Organisms

GM plants can improve <u>crop yields</u>. Many people in the world <u>suffer</u> from not being able to get <u>enough food</u>. Put these two bits of information together, and things might work out splendidly. Maybe.

Crops can be Genetically Modified to be Resistant to Insects

1) One reason why people might want to genetically engineer crops is to make them <u>resistant</u> to <u>insect pests</u>.

2) There's a bacterium called *Bacillus thuringiensis* (<u>Bt</u>) which produces a <u>toxin</u> (poison) that <u>kills</u> many of the <u>insect larvae</u> that are <u>harmful</u> to crops.

3) The <u>gene</u> for the <u>Bt toxin</u> is <u>inserted</u> into crops, like <u>corn</u> and <u>cotton</u>, which then produce the toxin in their <u>stems</u> and <u>leaves</u> — making them <u>resistant</u> to the insect pests.

4) The toxin is <u>specific</u> to insect pests — it's <u>harmless to humans</u>, <u>animals</u> and <u>other insects</u>. However, the <u>long-term</u> effects of exposure to Bt crops <u>aren't yet known</u>.

5) The insects that feed on the crops are <u>constantly exposed</u> to the <u>toxin</u>, so there's a danger they'll develop <u>resistance</u> and <u>no longer be killed</u> by it. Farmers try to <u>avoid</u> this happening by using <u>other insecticides</u> too.

Some People in Developing Countries Don't Have Enough Food

Many people in the world today don't have <u>enough</u> food to eat (or the diet they have isn't <u>varied</u>). This mostly happens in <u>developing countries</u> — like those in <u>Africa</u> and parts of <u>Asia</u>.

Biotechnology could help...

1) Crops can be genetically engineered to be <u>resistant to pests</u> — improving crop yields.

2) They can be genetically engineered to <u>grow better</u> in <u>drought conditions</u> — again improving crop yields.

3) And some crops can be engineered to combat certain <u>deficiency diseases</u>, e.g. '<u>Golden Rice</u>' has been <u>genetically engineered</u> to produce a chemical that's converted in the body to <u>vitamin A</u>.

...But not everyone agrees

1) Many people argue that people go hungry because they <u>can't afford</u> to buy food, not because there <u>isn't</u> any food about. So they argue that you need to <u>tackle poverty first</u>.

2) There are fears that countries may become <u>dependent</u> on <u>companies</u> who <u>sell</u> GM seeds.

3) Sometimes <u>poor soil</u> is the main reason why <u>crops fail</u>, and even GM crops <u>won't survive</u>.

Developed Countries have Different Health Problems...

<u>Heart disease</u> and some <u>cancers</u> are pretty common health problems in developed countries like the UK and the USA — partly thanks to our unhealthy lifestyles. GM plants could help us with these <u>problems</u> too...

Genetically engineered tomatoes could have 'anti-cancer' properties...

1) <u>Snapdragon flowers</u> contain a type of <u>flavonoid</u>. Flavonoids are molecules found in many plants that have <u>antioxidant effects</u>, which are thought to protect against <u>cancers</u> and <u>heart disease</u>.

2) Scientists have genetically engineered <u>purple tomatoes</u> so that they contain the <u>flavonoid gene</u> from the snapdragon. (Don't ask me why they've suddenly turned <u>purple</u> — it's to do with the flavonoid.)

3) Purple tomatoes have been developed as an <u>easy way</u> to get <u>antioxidants</u> to people in developed countries, who tend <u>not</u> to eat enough fruit and vegetables (tut tut).

...But they have their problems too

1) The flavonoid might slightly <u>change the flavour</u> of the tomato.

2) Some people are worried about the <u>long-term effects</u> of GM crops. Have a look back at page 46 for a reminder about the <u>issues</u> surrounding GM crops.

If only there was a gene to make revision easier...

GM crops have the potential to help us solve all sorts of different <u>health problems</u> — anything from <u>malnutrition</u> to <u>heart disease</u>. But they're not without their <u>problems</u>. And you need to know both sides of the story...

Feeding More People

As the population of planet Earth increases, growing enough food for everyone isn't going to get any easier...

Not Everyone Has 'Food Security'

1) The world's population is rising very quickly.

2) This means that global food production must increase too so that we all have enough food to eat, with the right balance of nutrition — this is known as 'food security'.

3) According to the United Nations World Food Programme, in 2000-02 there were 852 million undernourished people worldwide. Of these, 815 million lived in developing countries.

4) As the world's population continues to grow we need to grow more food, so that each person still has the same amount of food to eat.

There are Various Ways you can Increase Food Production...

① Reducing Pest Numbers

1) Killing insect pests means crops grow larger, which means productivity is greater.

2) Farmers can reduce pest numbers by using insecticides, which kill insect pests that eat and damage crops.

3) Some plants can be genetically modified to produce toxins that kill the pests that feed on them. You've already read about crops that produce Bt toxin (see page 103).

4) Crop rotation (growing a cycle of different crops in a field each year) can stop the pests that affect one particular crop building up in an area.

5) Some farmers use biological control — this means using living things instead of chemicals to control a pest. E.g. aphids are a pest because they eat vegetables. Ladybirds are aphid predators, so they can be released into fields to keep aphid numbers down.

② Selective Breeding Programmes

Selective breeding is when humans select the best plants according to what we want from them. This is the basic process involved in selective breeding:

1) The parent plants with the best characteristics are selected, e.g. wheat plants with a high wheat yield (large ears).

2) They're bred with each other.

3) The best of the offspring are selected and bred.

4) This process is repeated over several generations to develop the desired traits, e.g. to produce a plant that has a very high yield of wheat.

Large ears × Breed → Very large ears

③ Genetically Modifying Plants

Another way of increasing food production is to use GM plants — after the last couple of pages, you should really be an expert in this by now...

Please sir — can I have some more...

... some more nutritious grub though please, not any of that 'orrible gruel stuff that was around in Dickens' time. Anyway, your treat for finishing this page is that you get to revise all about the ways that you can produce more food for a ever-growing world population. How to distribute all the food evenly, well that's a whole other issue...

Biofuels

We humans beings use an awful lot of <u>energy</u> — and that means burning lots of <u>fuel</u> to produce it. Scientists are always on the lookout for <u>new fuels</u> to burn that won't damage the <u>environment</u> as much as fossil fuels. And that's where <u>biofuels</u> come in...

Biofuels are Fuels Made from Biomass

<u>Biofuels</u> are made from <u>plants</u>, <u>animals</u>, or their <u>waste products</u>.
Here are three <u>examples</u> of biofuels that you might come across:

Biogas
1) Microorganisms <u>decompose</u> waste material or plants to produce <u>biogas</u>.
2) Biogas is usually about 70% <u>methane</u> and 30% <u>carbon dioxide</u>.
3) It can be <u>burned</u> to power a <u>turbine</u> (which can be used to <u>generate electricity</u>) or to <u>heat water</u> and produce <u>steam</u> to heat <u>central heating systems</u>.
4) It can also be used as a <u>fuel</u> for <u>cars</u> and <u>buses</u>.

Ka-boom

Biodiesel
1) Biodiesel is an <u>alternative fuel</u>, similar to regular diesel, which can be used in <u>vehicles</u> — the good thing is that you don't really need to alter the vehicle very much for it to run on biodiesel.
2) Biodiesel is made from made from <u>vegetable oils</u>, <u>animal fats</u> or <u>waste cooking oil</u>.

Ethanol
1) <u>Ethanol</u> can be burnt as <u>fuel</u>. It's a <u>cleaner fuel</u> than petrol or diesel, producing <u>fewer pollutants</u>.
2) <u>Ethanol</u> is produced by using yeast to <u>ferment glucose</u>. Materials like <u>sugar cane</u>, <u>corn</u> and <u>barley</u> can be used as a source of glucose in ethanol production.
3) <u>Cars</u> can be adapted to run on a <u>mixture of ethanol and petrol</u> — known as '<u>gasohol</u>'.

GASOHOL

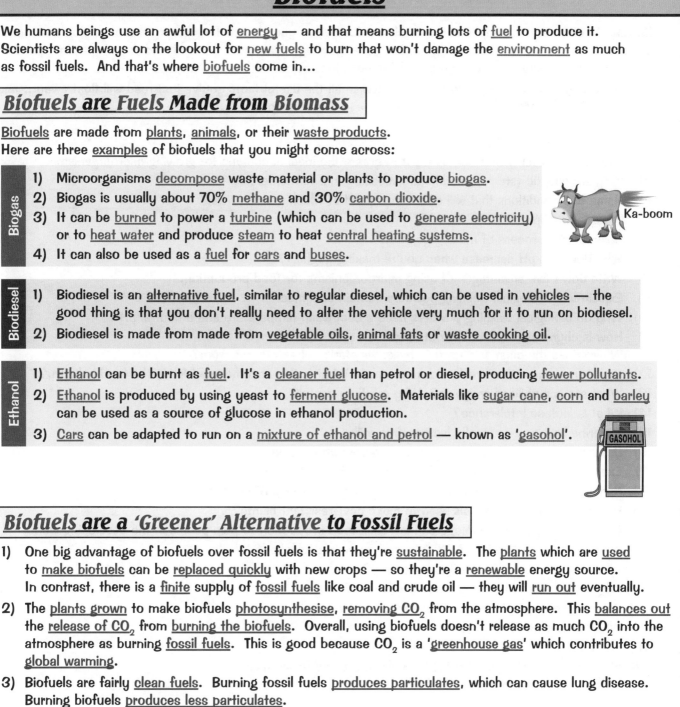

Biofuels are a 'Greener' Alternative to Fossil Fuels

1) One big advantage of biofuels over fossil fuels is that they're <u>sustainable</u>. The <u>plants</u> which are <u>used</u> to <u>make biofuels</u> can be <u>replaced quickly</u> with new crops — so they're a <u>renewable</u> energy source. In contrast, there is a <u>finite</u> supply of <u>fossil fuels</u> like coal and crude oil — they will <u>run out</u> eventually.

2) The <u>plants grown</u> to make biofuels <u>photosynthesise</u>, <u>removing CO_2</u> from the atmosphere. This <u>balances out</u> the <u>release of CO_2</u> from <u>burning the biofuels</u>. Overall, using biofuels doesn't release as much CO_2 into the atmosphere as burning <u>fossil fuels</u>. This is good because CO_2 is a '<u>greenhouse gas</u>' which contributes to <u>global warming</u>.

3) Biofuels are fairly <u>clean fuels</u>. Burning fossil fuels <u>produces particulates</u>, which can cause lung disease. Burning biofuels <u>produces less particulates</u>.

4) The use of biofuels <u>doesn't</u> produce significant amounts of sulfur dioxide, which can cause <u>acid rain</u>. This is produced by power plants which burn fossil fuels.

5) However, <u>growing</u> the crops needed to make biofuels takes up <u>large amounts of land</u>. This means there'll be <u>less land</u> available for growing crops for <u>food</u>, which could be a <u>problem</u>... as we need to feed more people (see previous page).

6) Also, things like power stations and vehicles need to be <u>adapted</u> to run on biofuels — this takes <u>time</u> and <u>costs money</u>.

You can make biogas too — just eat some lentils...

<u>Energy use</u> is a big problem in the modern world. Everybody wants a <u>car</u> and lots of nice shiny <u>gadgets</u> to make their lives easier. Trouble is, we've got to work out how to get everyone the energy they want to power all this stuff without completely <u>destroying the planet</u> along the way. So <u>biofuels</u> might just come in handy...

Revision Summary for B3 Topic 3

Hurrah. You've almost completed the whole book. Before you close it forever, try these revision questions. Do them all and check your answers. If you get any wrong, then learn those bits again, and do the questions again. Keep on going until you can get all the questions right.

It's a hard slog, but you've got to do it. Otherwise all the useful facts you've just read will float away... and you'll be left with nothing but a vague mental image of a fermenter.

1) What is a fermenter?
2) Explain how a fermenter can be used to create the ideal conditions for growing microorganisms.
3) Why are aseptic (sterile) conditions necessary in a fermenter?
4) Name two conditions that will affect the speed at which yeast grows.
5) What is mycoprotein used for?
6) Describe the process of making yoghurt.
7) Why does the pH decrease when you're making yoghurt?
8) Write down five advantages of using microorganisms for food production.
9) Explain why biological washing powders contain enzymes.
10) Why do biological washing powders need a cool wash temperature and a neutral pH?
11) How is chymosin traditionally obtained?
    Where does the chymosin used to make vegetarian cheese come from?
12) Name an enzyme that breaks down sucrose. What is this enzyme used for in the food industry?
13) What are immobilised enzymes? Why are they useful?
14) What is lactose intolerance?
15) Describe how you can make lactose-free milk.
16) Describe how you can use pectinase to extract apple juice.
17) Explain how GM organisms can be engineered to produce human insulin.
18) Name the bacterium that can be used as a vector to make GM plants.
19) How is *Bacillus thuringiensis* used to make pest-resistant plants?
20) Give three ways biotechnology can increase food production to help people in the developing world.
21) What are purple tomatoes? Why have they been developed?
22) What is meant by the term 'food security'?
23) Why do we need to increase food production?
24) Name three ways you can increase food production.
25) What are biofuels?
26) Name three biofuels.
27) a) List four advantages of using biofuels over using fossil fuels.
    b) List two disadvantages of biofuels.

Index

Index and Answers

Answers

Revision Summary for B1 Topic 1 (page 17)

8)   E.g. 1. Does it have a shell?
                - Yes — it's a snail
                - No — go to question 2.
            2. Does it have legs?
                - No — it's a worm
                - Yes — go to question 3.
            3. Does it have more than 8 legs?
                - Yes — it's a centipede
                - No — it's a spider.

23) BB and bb

Revision Summary for B1 Topic 2 (page 26)

16) a) BMI = $58 \div (1.5)^2 = 58 \div 2.25$
            $= 25.7777... = 25.8$
      b) No, Sophie isn't obese (her BMI is under 30).

Revision Summary for B2 Topic 1 (page 51)

3) $\times 25$ magnification

15) a) pH 1.6
      b) stomach

Revision Summary for B2 Topic 2 (page 60)

6)   a) 60 beats per minute
      b) 2 minutes
      c) 70 beats per minute

Revision Summary for B3 Topic 1 (page 85)

13) 1/2 (or 0.5 or 50%)